November 1984

❧ Treating ❧ the Long-Term Mentally Ill

Beyond Deinstitutionalization

H. Richard Lamb

Treating
the Long-Term
Mentally Ill

❧ ❧

Jossey-Bass Publishers

San Francisco • Washington • London • 1982

TREATING THE LONG-TERM MENTALLY ILL
Beyond Deinstitutionalization
   by H. Richard Lamb

Copyright © 1982 by: Jossey-Bass Inc., Publishers
                      433 California Street
                      San Francisco, California 94104

                            &

                      Jossey-Bass Limited
                      28 Banner Street
                      London EC1Y 8QE

Library of Congress Cataloging in Publication Data

Lamb, H. Richard, 1929–
      Treating the long-term mentally ill.

      Bibliography: p. 221
      Includes index.
      1. Mentally ill—Care and treatment—United States.
2. Chronically ill—Care and treatment—United. States.
3. Community mental health services—United States.
I. Title. [DNLM: 1. Community psychiatry. 2. De-
institutionalization. 3. Mental disorders—Therapy.
WM 30.6 L2128t]
RC480.53.L53   362.2'0973   82-48391
ISBN 0-87589-553-0

Manufactured in the United States of America

The paper in this book meets the guidelines for
permanence and durability of the Committee on
Production Guidelines for Book Longevity of the
Council on Library Resources.

JACKET DESIGN BY WILLI BAUM

FIRST EDITION

Code 8244

The Jossey-Bass
Social and Behavioral Science Series

✥ Foreword ✥

In post–World War II America a variety of civil rights protests gained widespread support. Reaching their peak expression in the 1960s, these initiatives were ideologically committed to improving the lot of individuals perceived as helpless in gaining access to life's entitlements. Like other civil rights protests of that era, the movement to deinstitutionalize chronic mental patients emphasized the inalienable rights of the mentally ill and their legitimate claims on society. Deinstitutionalization sought to exchange treatment in physically isolated settings for services provided in patients' home communities on the assumption that community-based treatment is both more humane and more therapeutic. The physical isolation of patients was understood to be inevitably accompanied by an invidious social exclusion that had to be corrected; and those who pioneered in deinstitutionalization efforts objected to both the content and the quality of care in large mental hospitals.

Other factors also exerted a profound influence on treatment ideology for the chronically mentally ill. The ability of social reformers to ally with fiscal conservatives in a rare coalition of ideologies was certainly critical to the growing deinstitutionalization movement. Community-based care was widely believed to be more economical than institutional care. And, if community-based care was understood to be both better (more humane) and cheaper (less costly), how could its superiority be denied? The rapidly growing ability to contain patients' most distressing symptoms through new developments in psychopharmacology only reinforced the commitment of advocates to the basic desirability of emptying, and eventually closing, mental institutions.

There is ample evidence that the popularity of specific treatment ideologies for the chronically mentally ill tends to be cyclical. As Darold Treffert has written, psychiatry "revolves as it evolves." But the post-war deinstitutionalization initiative was unique in its scope and consequences. Never before in our history was this particular patient population splintered into so many fragments. The depopulation of mental institutions was accompanied by a shift in thinking that viewed any institutional tenure as a "failure" on the part of service providers and planners, and considerable effort was devoted to avoiding new admissions for previously unhospitalized individuals.

The result was an unprecedented array of chronically mentally ill persons with markedly different treatment and residential histories. Some were released from institutions after as many as five or six decades of residence; others, equally ill, were denied admission in the first place. Of those released, some were shunted to "mini-institutions," facilities where, by most measures, patients' quality of life deteriorated; others, showing a persistent dependency on institutional care, developed patterns of repeated readmission and discharge. In addition, substantial numbers of patients remained institutionalized—individuals who, even in an era that idealized the benefits of community-based care, were not deemed "good risks" for discharge.

All these patients—or would-be patients—represented fallout from the new policies, and a whole language came into fashion to describe their degree of fit to an emerging system (or, often more accurately, "nonsystem") of care. There were "revolving-door" patients to remind us of the gulf that inevitably separates an ideology from its practical implementation. Patients who fell through the cracks of a "fragmented" service system demonstrated that mental institutions serve many functions in addition to patient care and that some of these—such as asylum, respite, and social support—are very difficult to duplicate in noninstitutional settings. The quest for "support networks" that would help implement these functions emerged as a major planning emphasis, and "case management" became a rallying call for service planners who wished to "coordinate" services and advocate on patients' behalf. To ease the transition from hospital to "less restrictive" community-based services, innovative residential sites were developed—"quarterway," "halfway," and in some places even "fullway" houses. Treatment options such as "partial care" were encouraged in order to "normalize" patients.

Rarely was the new language used with precision, so that any term could be used to promote a cause. Anyone could define a buzzword to suit his own perceptions of what was appropriate and humane. It was inevitable that chaos would result, and it did. Ego-investment in specific approaches to patient care ran high and often resulted in deeply rooted territorial feelings that exacerbated service delivery difficulties. In short, despite noble intentions, the efforts of service planners often resulted in patient neglect, as more and more individuals endured severe barriers to treatment. And the chronically mentally ill, who were to have been the beneficiaries of a "bold new approach" to service delivery, continued to suffer from inadequate attention to their most basic needs.

To be sure, there were exceptions. Many chronically ill patients benefitted from the new emphasis in service delivery, and it is hardly my intent to minimize those programs that met with success. Indeed, the ability of such programs to transform the lives of the chronically mentally ill has reinforced the basic assumptions underlying the deinstitutionalization movement: that community-based care represents a highly therapeutic option for these patients; that communities have the potential for providing a full range of needed services for individuals with severe mental disabilities; and that communities may sometimes be encouraged to assume initiative and responsibility in the care of their most severely impaired members. By demonstrating that we can, in fact, attend to the needs of the chronically mentally ill in noninstitutional settings, these extraordinary programs have provided great hope for the future. It is not surprising, given the magnitude of our investment in the deinstitutionalization movement, that many prefer to point to these examples of success and not to dwell on the less encouraging results of our efforts.

Yet, there is widespread agreement that the chronically mentally ill in general are *not* being adequately and humanely served by existing service structures. We still have not dealt adequately with the need to provide for continuity in the care of the most seriously ill patients in most locations. In fact, treatment for these patients remains partial, fragmented, and uncoordinated. Indeed, many chronically mentally ill individuals are not even enrolled in the psychiatric service system, and increasing numbers of them are being found among our cities' vagrant populations. Others wander aimlessly between cities and between states, and into and out of rural areas. Deinstitutionalization has clearly created unanticipated program needs.

The gaps through which patients fall have somehow become wider and deeper because of the multiplicity of service sites and the growing number of agencies "in charge" of programs for chronic patients. Whatever else it may or may not have connoted, the old state hospital certainly made service delivery easy, because virtually everything that happened for these patients happened in one place. In sum, our struggle to provide appropriate and responsive community-based services to the chronically mentally ill is still very much uphill; and service delivery problems are much more complex than they were several decades ago.

For more than a decade the writings of H. Richard Lamb have offered both skillful diagnoses of the problems associated with deinstitutionalization and thoughtful insights into what is needed to reduce these problems. Lamb's ability to bring scholarly research and clinical skills together into highly readable treatises has long served as an inspiration to those who work with the chronically mentally ill. For many mental patients who recognize their own predicaments in the pages of his writings; for caregivers who have fallen prey to the burnout he describes in Chapter Fifteen of this volume; for family members who have sought, often in vain, to participate in the care of seriously ill relatives; and for a generation of students in psychiatry and allied disciplines whose dedication and vision are essential to the humane care of these patients—the writings of H. Richard Lamb have come to symbolize hope. A brilliant analyst of service delivery problems, Lamb remains throughout his writings a forthright and partisan advocate of the chronically ill mental patient. The patient is always and unequivocally his most basic concern.

It is gratuitous to suggest that, had we listened to Lamb earlier, we might not find ourselves today in the midst of such serious problems. Although his wisdom has over the years been available to those who should have been concerned, it was undoubtedly necessary for the emerging system of care to endure a certain amount of trial and error. Even the pronouncements of prophets must await society's readiness.

But if Lamb was ahead of his time in the past, this is surely a moment in history when we need his foresight, concern, and gentle wisdom, if we are to make up the deficits that characterize our system of care. At this time, when our service structures are in serious disarray, when the generous federal support that aided the early years of the deinstitutionalization movement has all but evaporated, it is important that we have the example of reasoned thinking and careful advocacy that Lamb provides.

This book thus comes at a particularly appropriate time. One by one in these pages, the difficulties inherent in service delivery fads are exposed. We are cautioned against pursuing patients' "freedom" blindly and warned not to charge them with responsibilities their illnesses make them incapable of handling. And, while skills training is presented as a highly desirable intervention for many inpatients (Lamb was an early proponent of rehabilitation therapy), we are repeatedly alerted to the dangers of "overselling" rehabilitation. Lamb makes it very clear that commitment to an ideology, to a school of thought, must never reign; what is best for each individual patient is what counts.

Throughout, Lamb deals sensitively and sympathetically with basic issues in patient care, and his concern is expressed in numerous eloquent passages. There is, he tells us, "no higher priority for the mental health professions than to serve long-term severely disabled patients." But nowhere is his sensitivity to patients' needs, his exquisite concern for their welfare, better reflected than in the discussion of psychotherapy (see Chapter Ten). Firmly persuaded that every patient has an intact portion of ego that can, and must, be engaged in psychotherapy, Lamb discusses the limitations of con-

ventional therapy for most chronic patients. He is clear in his support of the notion that the first task of psychotherapy for this
population is to provide the patient with a sense of mastery that will
enable him to cope with his drives and symptoms and with the
realities of his external environment. Traditional insight-oriented
therapies have limited relevance to the needs of most chronic patients, but this does not mean that insight should be abandoned. It is
possible, and important, to redefine the meaning of insight: with
chronic mental patients, insight must be "here-and-now and reality-
based" and must focus on such matters as the meaning of symptoms,
the effects of stress, the role and limits of medications in combat-
ing stress, and the need to understand and, if possible, to avoid
anxiety-producing situations.

Lamb is deeply troubled by the suffering of chronic mental
patients. While mental health services often strive to serve many
masters—patients, professionals, and the community at large—no
such ambiguities color Lamb's writing. He is squarely on the side of
the patients, and all other concerns are subservient.

Richard Lamb has exerted a powerful influence over my own
thinking and my work in conceptualizing issues in the care of the
chronically mentally ill. It is easy to understand why. He engages
whatever it is in me that responds to the suffering of my fellows.
Thus, while Lamb speaks to me, as he does to others, both emotionally and intellectually, it is clearly the former that takes precedence.
The result is that his carefully worded accounts of research results
serve to reinforce what is to me a more basic message: that every
chronically mentally ill person is a unique human being with a
legitimate claim to specialized treatment of the highest possible
quality.

This primary focus in his work places Lamb's other insights
in perspective: it is only in connection with a patient's entitlement
to a life of dignity that continuity of care becomes an important
issue, or that vocational education becomes a serious goal. From this
vantage point, Lamb attacks some basic misconceptions. His writings make it very clear that progress in patient care must be measured in terms of the patient's needs, abilities, and desires—and not
according to rigid external criteria. Every treatment must be patient-

specific; and it is in this context that we are able to understand that the locus of care—institution or community—is far less important than the substance of that care.

This singular dedication to patient needs infuses Lamb's writings with a unique humility. This is an author who eschews "quick fixes" and who chooses instead to study a problem and all its implications before suggesting solutions. Thus, in his discussion of young adult chronic patients in Chapter Seven, Lamb frankly acknowledges the limits of our knowledge. He writes that "we must often learn to wait until maturity has shifted the balance" for these patients, or until the reluctant patient "has found some way of turning to us." As he does at various points in the volume, Lamb cautions us to place our lack of knowledge in perspective. We must "minimize our disappointment if our offers of help are rejected; we need to accept that our powers of persuasion are limited." Not only is such honesty in a field where we are constantly bombarded with quick-and-easy solutions refreshing; it is also a sign of hope, for it is only when we admit our limits that we can expect to expand our horizons.

Some will take issue with certain of Lamb's more controversial notions. His support of involuntary treatment for reluctant patients who require structure will not be endorsed by those who place patients' "civil rights" above all other concerns. Similarly, his notion that the case manager "should not be simply a broker of services but . . . should be the patient's primary therapist and the person who works with the family" will meet with argument. There are many dedicated service providers who feel that the primary therapist cannot be uniformly depended on to provide the time and support necessary for patient advocacy and case monitoring. To such critics I would suggest a careful rereading of Lamb's work. The essence of Lamb's position on case management, for example, is not related to any thought of intrinsic superiority of therapists but rather to a realistic concern that "major problems can result when persons . . . have power without clinical responsibility." Even those with an opposing view must honor this caveat. It is precisely because Lamb elevates issues to this higher level of concern that his work is so powerful.

H. Richard Lamb is clearly a master of his subject. He combines his skills as a clinician and researcher with deep outrage at a
system of care that often ascribes to the chronically mentally ill the
status of outcast. For many readers this volume will come as a welcome and critically needed summary and expansion of the seminal
ideas of an extraordinary author and human being.

September 1982   *Leona L. Bachrach, Ph.D.*
                              Professor of Psychiatry (Sociology)
                           Maryland Psychiatric Research Center
                        University of Maryland School of Medicine

❧ Preface ❧

This book has grown out of my experiences in working with the chronically mentally ill for more than twenty years. When I began to write the chapters four years ago, I decided to concentrate on the topics individually—to devote sufficient time to think about and to gather data on each aspect of work with long-term patients. In the process, I discussed segments of the book with colleagues, spoke on the subjects at various times, and published individual pieces in journals and other publications. I wanted time to refine my ideas, to obtain feedback from others in the field, and then to polish the material before publication in book form. The data gathering yielded new findings in many cases, and the feedback helped me broaden my perspectives on various topics. Both the new findings and the objectivity I gained helped me immensely as I revised and expanded the segments into an integrated and comprehensive whole—one that is intended to be a thoughtful, and thought-provoking, assessment of the issues involved in understanding and treating the long-term mentally ill.

The common themes that run throughout this book are set forth in the first chapter. Our attention then turns to a detailed look at a number of subjects necessary to understanding the chronically mentally ill and treating them in the community.

Chapter Two explores the possible roots of neglect of the long-term mentally ill, takes up some of the problems of dealing with chronic dependency, and discusses the issues that emerge when we try to set realistic goals for rehabilitation.

Chapter Three deals with deinstitutionalization. I begin with a brief history of this momentous social phenomenon and then go on to describe its accomplishments and its shortcomings. After analyzing some of the proposed solutions to these problems, I offer my own perspectives on the realities of deinstitutionalization and the broad issues upon which its success depends. Making deinstitutionalization work is in the last analysis the central concern of this book.

Chapter Four deals with a cornerstone of the long-term patient's survival in the community: living arrangements. Four supportive living situations are described: board-and-care homes, foster care, Fairweather's sheltered subsociety, and satellite housing. These four living arrangements are used to illustrate many of the issues and problems encountered in providing suitable community housing for long-term patients.

Since a large proportion of the chronically mentally ill live in nonmedical community residential facilities run by administrators and staff not specifically trained in the management of psychiatric patients, consultation to residential facilities is an issue of high priority. Chapter Five, "Consultation to Residential Care Facilities," explains what mental health consultants to these facilities need to know and, moreover, what they need to convey to both administrators and staff.

Chapter Six, "The Therapeutic Use of Structure," emphasizes that some severely disabled patients present major problems in management and can survive outside of state hospitals only if they have a sufficiently structured facility in the community. After describing the characteristics of these patients, I discuss the locked skilled-nursing facility with special programs for psychiatric patients as an alternative to the state hospital for many of these difficult patients.

Young chronic patients are faced with the same concerns and life-cycle stresses as others in their age group. Lacking the ability to withstand stress and cope with intimacy, they struggle and often fail. Chapter Seven, "Young Adult Chronic Patients: The New Drifters," recounts these struggles and takes up such issues as facing the crisis of age thirty, problems of control and violence, and why these persons drift. Approaches to these problems are also discussed: working with young adult patients while they may still be motivated to make changes, accepting that involving them in treatment may be a long and difficult process, helping them develop appropriate rationalizations to maintain their self-esteem, and supporting realistic goals.

Families of schizophrenics have received too little help from mental health professionals, even though families are the primary care agents for a large proportion of long-term patients. Chapter Eight, "Families of the Mentally Ill," describes some of the problems that occur in living with long-term patients. The chapter then takes up a new and positive development: the mutual support and advocacy groups that have been formed by relatives of patients nationwide. As we will see, mental health professionals can help families of schizophrenics by providing practical realistic advice on how to deal with the illness. The chapter also describes an educational approach that is increasingly being used by mental health professionals who work with schizophrenics and their families.

Chapter Nine, "The Mentally Ill in Jail," begins with a study of mentally ill inmates in an urban county jail and describes the characteristics of this severely disturbed group. Why have inmates been arrested rather than hospitalized? Has there been "criminalization" of the mentally ill? After taking up these issues the chapter then turns to what I perceive as a need for more voluntary and involuntary treatment for these patients in the community.

Maintaining a personal, individualized approach to each patient is emphasized throughout the book. Chapter Ten, "Individual Psychotherapy," and Chapter Eleven, "Case Management," stress the importance of mental health workers establishing and maintaining one-to-one relationships with long-term patients. In such relationships we should deal with reality issues and focus on the importance of understanding each individual's strengths and specific vulnerabilities. The concepts and techniques of individual psychotherapy with the chronically mentally ill are treated in detail in Chapter Ten. Chapter Eleven explains why "case managers" must be more than mere brokers of service.

Income maintenance programs for the chronically and severely mentally ill are clearly very much needed, but they also have adverse effects. In Chapter Twelve, "Supplemental Security Income: Benefits and Problems," I examine both the importance of these programs and the problems they create.

The day treatment center is a crucial resource for the chronically mentally ill—not only as an alternative to hospitalization but also as the nucleus of a community network of services for the rehabilitation and management of long-term patients. Chapter Thirteen, "Day Treatment Centers," examines the functions of the day treatment center and then explores a number of clinical issues in the day treatment center itself and also in aftercare.

Chapter Fourteen, "Social Rehabilitation," argues that social rehabilitation programs should be set up outside of mental health settings and should be staffed whenever possible by nonprofessionals—community volunteers, teachers, recreation department personnel. The chapter describes a number of these programs that work.

Chapter Fifteen, "Avoiding Staff Burnout," addresses an issue of increasing concern as more and more mental health personnel work with the chronically mentally ill. This chapter cites some of the factors leading to staff burnout and then suggests ways of avoiding it.

Finally, much credit is due my wife and colleague, Doris Lamb, whose ideas and suggestions have contributed to almost every part of this book. And I wish to express appreciation to my secretary, Dorese Berg, for her invaluable assistance in all aspects of the book's preparation.

Los Angeles, California   H. Richard Lamb
September 1982

❧ Contents ❧

Part Three: Working with the Underserved

Part Four: Individualizing Treatment

Part Five: Improving Access to Treatment

❧ The Author ❧

H. Richard Lamb is professor of psychiatry and the behavioral sciences at the University of Southern California School of Medicine. He received the B.A. degree from the University of Pennsylvania (1950) and the M.D. degree from Yale University (1954); he took his psychiatric residency training at Yale, completing it in 1958.

For sixteen years prior to joining the University of Southern California in 1976, Lamb was involved full-time in community mental health in San Mateo County, California. During this period he served in a variety of clinical and administrative capacities— specifically in psychiatric inpatient, outpatient, and day treatment services; he also consulted and collaborated with public health nursing, the welfare department, and various parts of the criminal justice system, including the police and probation department. He developed comprehensive vocational rehabilitation services for psychiatric patients and was active in organizing a variety of housing arrangements for psychiatric patients through a private nonprofit agency.

Lamb's research and writing has focused on the long-term, severely disabled, mentally ill—to some extent in state hospitals but primarily in the community. His interests and writings, however, have ranged over most areas of community mental health and have included attempts to conceptualize and clarify the issues in primary prevention, work with the criminal justice system, and alternatives to acute hospitalization. He has been an expert witness for the plaintiffs in litigations involving the rights of psychiatric patients, among them *Wyatt* v. *Stickney* and *Dixon* v. *Weinberger*. He has been involved with organizations of families of the mentally ill since the early 1970s.

Lamb is a member of the Committee on Rehabilitation of the American Psychiatric Association. He is editor-in-chief of *New Directions for Mental Health Services,* a quarterly journal, and has published three previous books with Jossey-Bass: *Handbook of Community Mental Health Practice* (1969), *Rehabilitation in Community Mental Health* (1971) and *Community Survival for Long-Term Patients* (1976).

Lamb is currently continuing his research on the mentally ill in the criminal justice system.

❧ Treating ❧ the Long-Term Mentally Ill

Beyond Deinstitutionalization

❦ One ❦

Some Common Themes

This book is in many ways a personal statement. In the following pages I present my own point of view and offer perspectives emerging from my own experience on a number of issues I consider central to the understanding, treatment, and rehabilitation of long-term severely disabled psychiatric patients in the community.

A number of common themes run throughout the book. I assume, for example, that there is a need to explore *all* avenues of inquiry in the quest for understanding what the long-term patient needs. If we approach the subject with preconceived notions of how things are and how they should be, obvious solutions that literally leap out at us may go ignored if they run contrary to our ideology. I can think of no better issue to illustrate this point than that of individual freedom. One may wholeheartedly believe in freedom for the individual, as I do, and also believe, as I do, that one of the most important gains of deinstitutionalization has been an increased degree of liberty for most psychiatric patients. At the same time I believe we should remain alert for situations where patients can be harmed by being given more freedom than they can handle. This belief is not a betrayal of an ideal; it is simply a clinical reality. But if we are not willing to bend to the demands of reality, we are less able to help our patients. In the meantime, we find our effectiveness limited to a smaller and smaller group of patients. Worse, many patients whom we cannot bring ourselves to deprive of some of their

1

liberty by means of well chosen limits in the community will find themselves in jails and state hospitals where they have lost all their liberty. We will have remained true to our ideology, but the patients will have paid the price.

Moreover, one needs to listen to what our patients are trying to tell us —to look beyond the conventional wisdom of the field and question the consensus of our colleagues. Otherwise, how is our profession to grow and to progress? We may find the consensus to be correct after all, but often we will see things from a fresh perspective.

There is no higher priority for the mental health profession, I think, than to serve long-term severely disabled patients. Fortunately, this view is now shared by many in our field. Too often lacking, however, is the allocation of funds to implement programs that will make this view a reality and not simply a theoretical position. To a large extent we already know what kind of community programs are needed to raise the level of functioning of these patients and to enhance the quality of their lives. But we cannot even accomplish the first step of providing an adequate supportive living situation if our funding is only at the level of a Supplemental Security Income (SSI) grant plus a small amount of mental health funds. We have only to compare the SSI grant on a per diem basis with that of hospitals or even the Medicaid rate for skilled nursing facilities to see the impossibility of doing what is needed with the amount of money made available to us. In my opinion there is no more pressing issue in mental health today than the need for greatly increased funding for more and better living arrangements and treatment and rehabilitation programs for the chronically mentally ill.

Long-term patients are often discussed as if they were a homogeneous group. But as we will see throughout this book, they are a very heterogeneous group—in terms of their potential for functioning in the various areas in their lives, their ability to handle independence and cope with stress, and their need for support and structure. This theme will become clear as we discuss their potential for "normalization" (of their living and work situations and social milieu) and "mainstreaming" (entry into the mainstream of society) in Chapters Two and Fifteen.

As I have said elsewhere (Lamb, 1976), I believe that high (but realistic) expectations should be maintained so that patients strive to reach their full social and vocational potential, even though this potential may be limited. This philosophy encourages their participation in the community, enhances their self-esteem, and generally improves the quality of their lives. Although it is important to expect people to realize their potential, it is equally important not to expect more than they can realistically achieve, or we may be setting them up for another failure (Allen, 1975). High expectations are frequently confused with unrealistic expectations. This confusion is frequently seen in the vocational goals formulated for long-term, severely disabled patients and in the degree of independence expected of some in their living situations. All too often, we lack an accurate assessment of patients' current capabilities and sufficient flexibility in our programs to take account of their limitations. As a result patients are often asked to do more than is possible for them at the time. This theme emerges in many ways. Unrealistic goals affect staff as well as patients, as we will see in Chapter Fifteen on staff burnout. Moreover, instead of blaming ourselves for expecting too much we tend to blame the patients for disappointing and frustrating us.

The pace at which the long-term patient is able to change or improve is a slow one (Allen, 1974). Frequently we forget this and push our patients too far and too fast. Sometimes we are misled by a facade of strength that exaggerates the patient's actual capabilities. Sometimes the patient or therapist denies the extent of the problem. Perhaps the parents have had difficulty accepting—and letting the patient accept—his or her limitations. Perhaps the patient believes that anything short of quick success means failure. Perhaps the therapist overidentifies with the patient and loses sight of what are realistic goals and how fast patients can move toward them. Long-term patients must learn to pace themselves so that they do not attempt to accomplish in a given period more than they are able. Their progress may be slow, but they, and we, must learn to accept this. Otherwise they may push themselves, or be pushed, into a situation where the only escape is a flight back into illness. One of the most beneficial things we can do for long-term patients is to help them see that they must pace themselves and then to help them learn how.

If we are unsure of a patient's capabilities, a higher goal—say, an earlier entry into the work world—can be opted for. In this case, the patient should be observed carefully to see if he or she can handle the added stress or whether the goals need to be lowered.

Nothing is more important than taking a personal, individualized approach to each patient. This theme will be found throughout this book and especially in the chapters on individual psychotherapy and case management. Too often, the uniqueness of each individual gets lost in a group aftercare program or a bureaucratized case management system.

Continuity of care is clearly a goal in all aspects of the treatment and rehabilitation of long-term patients (Bachrach, 1981a). If that continuity cannot be maintained with the same individual caregiver, it should at least be maintained with the same agency. We will see some of the advantages of ongoing long-term treatment relationships in Chapter Thirteen when we discuss an aftercare program at a day treatment center. In outpatient treatment we come to know our patients better, and they us, as the years go by. Not only do we recognize problems more quickly but we learn to anticipate them. And we find that a twenty-year relationship with a chronically mentally ill patient and his family can be for us a gratifying relationship indeed. In some respects our patients become like old friends, and we experience the profound professional satisfaction that many family physicians have found in their enduring relationships with patients.

Another theme that runs throughout this book is the importance of taking the *family* into account—working with them, not blaming them, educating them about the nature and management of their relative's illness. Families generally need our help and deserve it. Moreover, our work with them will more often than not benefit the patient. Further, families can be among our most effective allies in securing services for our patients.

Structure is often a neglected ingredient of community treatment. Some severely disabled patients present major problems in management and can survive outside of state hospitals only if they have a sufficiently structured situation in the community. While most patients need only a small to moderate amount of structure, others need a highly structured environment. What constitutes structure? This question is addressed in Chapter Four and again, more fully, in Chapter Six. Our society and the mental health professions declare that individuals should structure their own lives and not have others do it for them. Some patients, however, need considerable structure to compensate for their lack of internal controls and give them a sense of security. This need is neither good nor bad; it is simply a clinical reality requiring a clinical judgment that should not be influenced by ideology.

It has been my experience that treatment and rehabilitation begin with appropriately supportive and structured living arrangements. These arrangements may run the gamut from independent living to halfway houses and board-and-care homes to locked facilities. Treatment and rehabilitation are of little avail until the patient feels secure in a stabilized living situation.

This book's orientation is clearly psychosocial. But this does not mean that we may ignore psychoactive medication; psychosocial treatment and psychoactive medication are not antithetical but complementary. Furthermore, it is my belief that treatment in the community of a large proportion of long-term patients would be impossible without the modern psychoactive medications. There is now widespread recognition that pharmacotherapy, as well as the flowering of the psychosocial approach, has played a leading role in bringing about modern community treatment.

Psychoactive medications provide crucial ego support for the patient dealing with both the routine stresses and the crises of life. Nevertheless, some mental health professionals still hesitate to support the use of medication. Some argue that change should take place through insight and the interaction of therapist and patient or therapeutic milieu and patient. Some are concerned about patients becoming too dependent on medication. Others object to measures they believe to be only "symptomatic." Still others fear that the use of psychoactive medications will undermine the psychosocial approach. These arguments are not entirely without merit, but they seem like academic luxuries when a therapist watches a patient grow progressively more psychotic and in need of hospitalization while the insight he is waiting for becomes a full-blown thought disorder (Lamb, 1975). The evidence is now overwhelming that the use of psychoactive medications has not just a significant but a striking effect on the relapse rate of schizophrenic patients (Davis, 1975; Hogarty and Ulrich, 1977; Appleton, 1982).

Some of the adverse effects of psychoactive medications are serious indeed. Tardive dyskinesia is one. Further, Estroff (1981) observes that being given medication is interpreted by the mentally ill as a message that they are crazy people who will never get well. She thinks that side effects contribute to patients' looking different, and therein lies the paradox of medications—they keep you from being "crazy," but they reveal your "crazy" identity and defects to others. This does not mean that we should stop dispensing psychoactive medications. Far from it. But we do need a balanced view of the results of our ministrations so that we can minimize adverse effects and weigh the costs against the benefits.

Another theme that runs through this book is that goals should be clearly defined in all aspects of treatment for each long-term patient. Then efforts become purposeful rather than diffuse. Knowing what we are trying to achieve enables us to focus on *how* to reach our goals. For instance, if we ask therapists why they are seeing the patient individually, they often answer "I am doing therapy" as if no further explanation were necessary. But what are the goals? The importance of conceptualizing our aims in individual psychotherapy will emerge in Chapter Ten. And throughout the book I emphasize that we must conceptualize our work with long-term patients in a practical way.

Is the period of treatment time-limited because of the setting, as in an acute hospital or an acute day treatment center? If so, our goals need to be set accordingly and matters should be discussed that can be resolved in the time available. This principle applies to any treatment in any setting or time frame. In the chapter on day treatment we will see the problems that arise when short-term, limited goals—such as guiding the patient into remission, identifying the precipitating stresses, and formulating a treatment plan—are not differentiated from long-term, more far-reaching goals. The result is that patient and staff fail to distinguish the goals of the acute day treatment center from those more appropriate for aftercare. The center becomes a less effective resource and, lacking a clear understanding of its objectives, may keep the patient too long and foster undue dependency. Still another example is the sheltered workshop that becomes more effective and meaningful when patients and staff identify realistic goals and work toward them.

Work therapy geared to the capabilities of the individual patient should be a cornerstone of community treatment of long-term patients. While vocational rehabilitation is not for everyone, for many patients it can provide a considerable measure of fulfillment in what would otherwise be a life without meaning. Since vocational rehabilitation for psychiatric patients is described in great detail in my last two books, *Rehabilitation in Community Mental Health* (Lamb and Associates, 1971) and *Community Survival for Long-Term Patients* (Lamb and Associates, 1976), the reader is referred there for an exposition of this subject.

No theme in this book is more important than directing our efforts to giving patients a sense of mastery—the feeling that they can cope with their internal drives, their symptoms, and the demands of their environment. All treatment and rehabilitation should be designed to help long-term patients improve their ability to master and deal with both internal and external demands to the limits of their potential. With the development of mastery, patients achieve not only a better adaptation to their world but also a significant rise in self-esteem and sense of self-worth.

To attain our objective, we must work with the *well* part of the ego. Regardless of the extent of psychopathology in evidence, there is always an intact portion of the ego to which treatment and rehabilitation efforts can be directed (Lamb, 1971b). The goal is to expand the remaining well part of the person rather than to remove or cure pathology. The focus should be on the healthy part of the personality, the strengths of the person. Even though the pathology is left alone, when the healthy part of the personality is expanded, the person is better able to function (Beard, Goertzel, and Pearce, 1958).

Now that we have examined some of the central themes that run through the book, it is time to turn our attention to the details. In the next chapter we will see how attitudes toward the long-term mentally ill have changed over the years and the critical problems this shift in perspectives has brought.

ঞ্জ Two ঞ্জ

From Neglect to Rehabilitation

Neglect of the severely mentally ill, then outrage and movements for reform, followed again by a lapse into neglect—this has been a characteristic pattern in the mental health professions and society at large. Once again mental health professionals are rediscovering the neglect of the long-term severely mentally ill. Only a few decades have passed since we realized that, with our cooperation, mental patients were warehoused in the depersonalizing, dehumanizing atmosphere of huge state hospitals with all the disabling effects of institutionalism. Now we have discovered that we substituted one kind of neglect for another by shifting these patients to an unprepared and often unreceptive community where many are living impoverished lives. How could professionals trained in the understanding of human behavior, and with a major responsibility for the fate of the mentally ill, be so insensitive to the needs of their charges—not once but repeatedly?

In the mid-nineteenth century, psychiatric reformers, shocked by conditions for the mentally ill in the community, fought for humane hospitalization. Within a few decades the mentally ill had been forgotten and conditions in the hospitals steadily deteriorated. Then in the early twentieth century the psychiatric reform move-

Note: This chapter is a revised version of a paper by the author entitled "Roots of Neglect of the Long-Term Mentally Ill," *Psychiatry,* 1979, *42* (3), 201–207.

ment, catalyzed by the work of Clifford Beers and the mental hygiene societies, focused on the plight of the hospitalized mentally ill. Once public support and money were obtained, however, the movement turned to outpatient treatment and efforts at prevention in the community. Within a few decades the reformers had all but abandoned the hospitalized severely mentally disabled and "left the state hospital and its professional staff . . . at the bottom of the ladders of professional status and public esteem" (Quen, 1977, p. 11).

When the current furor and the heightened interest in the chronically mentally ill die down, will we once again turn away from them? To gain some understanding of this problem, suppose we examine some characteristics of the chronically disabled to see whether the explanation can be partly traced to the fact that their needs clash with our own. In addition to this clash of interests, or perhaps because of it, we may also misunderstand their needs. Further, do the severely mentally ill evoke reactions in us as members of the larger society that contribute to this repeated rejection?

Characteristics of the Severely Mentally Ill

The long-term severely mentally ill have been described as marginal, socially isolated, vocationally inadequate, and possessed of exaggerated dependency needs (Dincin, 1975; Simon, 1965). Obviously this is not always true, for many can attain relatively high levels of social and vocational functioning. But a sizable proportion find it difficult to meet even the simple demands of daily living. They are unable to withstand pressure and are apt to develop incapacitating psychiatric symptoms when confronted with the common crises of life. Many of the long-term mentally ill withdraw from work and social activities because they feel inadequate. Mental health professionals and community agencies can often build social and vocational skills, but there are limits to what they can accomplish; inability to tolerate even minimal stress is a severely limiting characteristic (Lamb, 1979b).

For a number of the long-term mentally ill, too many demands—and for some, any demands at all—will reactivate symptoms and perhaps necessitate a hospitalization. For many, however, too few demands and too low expectations result in regression. The work of Wing (1977, p. 27) "suggests that many patients who experience an attack of acute schizophrenia remain vulnerable to social stresses of two different kinds. On the one hand, too much social stimulation, experienced by the patient as social intrusiveness, may lead to an acute relapse. On the other hand, too little stimulation will exacerbate any tendency already present towards social withdrawal, slowness, underactivity, and an apparent lack of motivation. Thus, the patient has to walk a tightrope between two different types of danger, and it is easy to become decompensated either way."

Murphy, Engelsmann, and Tcheng-Laroche (1976) consider it likely that many patients with chronic mental illness will lose their active symptoms more rapidly in a setting that is undemanding and permits them to limit involvement—in contrast to a setting that seeks to involve them in normal social intercourse and move them toward even partial independence. Psychoactive drugs and other community supports may also be required to ensure that patients are able to remain in the community. There is experimental evidence that many schizophrenics are unable to tolerate stressful family situations; rehospitalization is increased when the patients live with families that are hostile to them, critical, and emotionally overinvolved, as a reaction to the difficulties of living with schizophrenia (Brown, Birley, and Wing, 1972). Vaughn and Leff (1976) replicated these findings and showed that social withdrawal can be an effective way of coping with a stressful family situation, preserving the patient from relapse and readmission to the hospital. Schizophrenics, then, have a limited tolerance for stress in their social environment, and avoidance of stress is one way of attempting to survive outside of a hospital.

Nevertheless, I believe that normalization of the patient's environment and rehabilitation to the greatest extent possible should be a goal of treatment (Lamb, 1976). This environment should include the social milieu, the living situation, and the work situation. The patient's condition should not be allowed to set him or her apart from other citizens in our society. This ideal of normalization frequently cannot be achieved, however. Every patient should be given every opportunity to reach this goal, but we need to realize that a proportion of our patients will fall short of it. If we persist in fruitless efforts and attempt to adjust people to a life-style beyond their ability, not only may we cause them anguish but we run the risk of contributing to the emergence of manifest psychopathology. Moreover, we ourselves become frustrated and then angry at the patients. In the end we may reject them and abandon them to their accustomed state of neglect. Or, perhaps worse, we may continue to see them and expose them to the same stressful emotional tone and interaction they cannot handle with their own families.

Persons who spend long periods in hospitals develop what has come to be known as institutionalism—a syndrome characterized by lack of initiative, apathy, withdrawal, submissiveness to authority, excessive dependence on the institution, and feelings of worthlessness and dehumanization (Wing and Brown, 1970). This syndrome may not be entirely the outcome of living in and adapting to the institution; at least in part, it may be characteristic of the schizophrenic process itself (Johnstone and others, 1981). As Brown and others (1966) have pointed out, many patients who are liable to institutionalism may develop dependence on any other way of life that provides minimal social stimulation and allows them to be socially inactive; they gravitate toward a life-style that will allow them to remain free from symptoms and dysphoric feelings.

Is this bad? For many it may lead to unnecessary regression and serve as an impediment to increasing their level of social and vocational functioning; it should thus be discouraged. But I think a case can be made that this restricted life-style meets the needs of many others and helps them maintain community tenure. Mental health professionals and society at large need to consider the crippling limitations of mental illness that do not yield to current treatment methods; they need to be unambivalent, moreover, about providing adequate care for this vulnerable group so that the end result is not like the fate of the mentally ill in the back wards of state hospitals. For those who can be restored only to a limited degree, we should provide reasonable comfort and an undemanding life with dignity. But such "limited" goals may not meet the needs of mental health professionals.

The Needs of Mental Health Professionals

Besides earning a livelihood, mental health professionals need to derive personal and professional satisfaction from their work. Most of us hope that our patients will show some change toward more effective adaptation and self-realization. We want the people we treat to become able to involve themselves with others in a gratifying way and to achieve increasing autonomy and the capacity for self-support.

Most professionals are able to respond to the dependency needs of their patients to at least some extent. In fact, in order to strengthen a therapeutic alliance, we often consciously or unconsciously encourage dependency at the beginning of treatment. When a patient seems arrested in a chronic dependency on the therapist, however, and makes "no progress"—when the gratification of the person's chronic dependency needs becomes a primary function of the treatment—most professionals feel frustrated because their own needs are not being met. They begin to have doubts about their healing ability. The refractory behavior of the patient, they fear, will reflect publicly their professional inadequacy. This frustration begets anger, and finally they find rationalizations to withdraw from the patient and refer him or her elsewhere.

This issue was illustrated in a successful and innovative community treatment program when the highly competent staff decided to reevaluate their program. As they reviewed their work with their long-term patients, they had to face the incontrovertible fact that many of them could not be rehabilitated vocationally and an appreciable number not even socially. Now these previously enthusiastic professionals and paraprofessionals became depressed. The necessity of having to lower their goals and to recognize that some people can only tolerate a passive, inactive, and often isolated lifestyle was hard to accept. Some staff members never could come to terms with this insight and now, a year later, still deny the unpalatable truth in varying degrees.

The failure of many long-term patients to involve themselves in rehabilitation activities is often attributed to lack of motivation. A closer look reveals that these patients are afraid they will fail if they attempt such activities, and their apprehension is often well founded. To save face, they let others believe (and they themselves believe) that they have decided not to participate rather than admit that they are victims of their low self-esteem and are afraid to try. They would rather appear lazy than fearful and inadequate. This attitude creates a significant problem for them, however. According to Parsons (1951), the sick role is sanctioned in our society only if the person adopts the patient role and strives to overcome his or her problems and return to "normal functioning." To do otherwise is to invite social disapproval and rejection. Before labeling these persons "unmotivated," we should look more closely to determine whether "unwilling" should not be understood as "unable."

There tends to be a basic moral disapproval in our society of dependency, of a passive, inactive life-style, and of accepting public support instead of working. This attitude is probably another reason for the rejection and neglect of the mentally ill. Such a moral reaction is not limited to people with a right-wing social philosophy but seems to occur in all of us, even those of us who think of ourselves as progressive. Although as a rule we try to deny our disapproval, our moral reaction obfuscates the issues and interferes with the provision of appropriate care for the long-term and severely disabled mentally ill. Our dissatisfaction with a primary role of gratifying chronic dependency needs and a more or less covert moral rejection of our patients' surrender to passivity are probably two roots of our neglect of the mentally ill.

Sociocultural Realities

Other areas where we can find insights to help us understand our society's and our profession's repeated neglect of the mentally ill have been carefully explored and reported in the literature. In their 1950 study of relationships between social class and mental illness in New Haven, Hollingshead and Redlich (1958) found striking social class differences in the prevalence of psychoses. The occurrence of major mental illness was especially high in the lowest class (class V). These investigators also found a disinclination to treat patients from the lower social classes, regardless of diagnosis:

Practically all the therapists interviewed disapproved of the dominant behavior patterns in the class V patients.

They were repelled by their crude, vulgar language, their
outbursts of violence, at times by their passivity and apathy,
or by their acceptance of such behavior as a husband beating
his wife and the wife taking the beating for granted, and their
endurance of poverty and economic insecurity. The therapists
were puzzled and upset over the sexual mores of their class V
patients. As a group, the psychiatrists were irritated by the
patients' inability to think in their terms. They complained
about the dullness and stupidity of these patients and particularly of their apathetic dependency. The following remarks
are illustrations of such attitudes: "Seeing him every morning
was a chore; I had to put him on my back and carry him for
an hour." "He had to get attention in large doses, and this
was hard to do." "The patient was not interesting or attractive; I had to repeat, repeat, repeat." "She was a poor, un-
happy, miserable woman—we were worlds apart" [1958, p.
344].

A subsequent study in New Haven for the years 1950–1960
indicated similar phenomena (Myers and Bean, 1968). While a great
deal has changed since then, there is evidence (Baekeland and
Lundwall, 1975) that much that was described then is still true
today; in keeping with the fashion of the times, however, such negative attitudes would today be expressed in more subtle ways. A disinclination to treat the lower social classes, where the preponderance
of the severely mentally ill can be found, may be yet another reason
why we turn away from them.

A related problem is that a large proportion of mental health
professionals have been educated for and oriented toward office psychotherapy without instruction on how to adapt their knowledge
and modify their techniques to suit either the severely disabled or
those from the lower classes. These issues are taken up in detail in
Chapter Ten. Moreover, those in private practice are often reluctant
to enrich their psychotherapy with collaboration with rehabilitation
and social agencies, collaboration for which they are not compensated. This holds true even in the states where Medicaid pays for
psychiatric outpatient treatment. In the remaining states, the severely disabled have even less access to the private practice community.

In their classic work *Closed Ranks*, Cumming and Cumming
(1957) report on a 1951 field survey in two small Canadian towns on

public attitudes toward mental illness. They found that people tried to deny the very existence of mental illness. Failing this, they tried to isolate the individual both socially and physically, usually in a hospital. Then they insulated themselves; they denied that the isolation of the deviant was a problem. Insulation, the Cummings theorized, made possible the community's remarkable tolerance for deplorable conditions in mental hospitals, the patients' isolation, and the community's rejection of ex-mental patients. These mechanisms also reduced the guilt of those who had had a family member sent off to a state hospital. The Cummings speculated that it was necessary to banish the mentally ill who deviated from the norms of society to ensure that the norms continued to be observed by those who remained, thereby maintaining the intactness of the social system. A 1974 replication of the study in one of the same towns revealed almost identical results (D'Arcy and Brockman, 1976).

Other studies of public attitudes toward mental illness (Lemkau and Crocetti, 1962; Meyer, 1964; Bentz, Edgerton, and Kherlopian, 1969; Crocetti, Spiro, and Siassi, 1971) have produced conflicting results. Lemkau and Crocetti, in the early 1960s, found in interviews of over 1,700 blue-collar residents of Baltimore what they considered understanding and tolerance for the mentally ill. Crocetti and colleagues interviewed almost a thousand people and concluded "responses to questions about social distance showed significantly greater acceptance than rejection of all those who were formerly mentally ill" (1971, p. 1121). A refinement of the methodology with the same sample suggested that acceptance or rejection of a patient depends less on the history of mental illness than on sociological characteristics such as social class, education, personal income, and physical appearance (Siassi, Spiro, and Crocetti, 1973).

Other studies (Phillips, 1966; Tringo, 1970) have painted a very different picture; they suggest that the mentally ill are still severely stigmatized and that the attitudes of the American public are still decidedly negative toward those with a history of psychiatric hospitalization; most people experience a distaste, even dread, of the mentally ill and a desire to maintain social distance from them. To complicate the issue further, doubts have been raised about the validity of research into attitudes toward mental illness (Rabkin, 1974)—in particular, what relationship exists, if any, between one's verbal statements of attitude and one's actual behavior if faced with a real situation involving the mentally ill?

Thus we cannot yet dismiss the phenomenon of closed ranks. Moreover, despite our training and orientation, we as mental health professionals are products of our culture and our society; we can hardly avoid subtly reinforcing and perpetuating the attitudes of the culture that shaped us in the first place. In many community mental health centers the ranks are indeed closed to the long-term, severely disabled mentally ill.

Overselling Rehabilitation

The recognition that so many of the long-term, severely mentally ill are leading impoverished lives in the community has led to an outcry for an array of services—to improve the quality of their lives, to raise the level of their social and vocational functioning, to integrate them into community life, and to give them identities of citizen, worker, or student rather than simply that of mental patient. Paul and Lentz (1977) have shown that intensive psychosocial intervention in the form of social learning therapy with chronically institutionalized patients can result in significant improvement in self-care, interpersonal and communication skills, and level of in-hospital functioning generally; there is often a corresponding reduction in bizarre behavior as well as a greater likelihood of release to the community. Their purpose was to prepare these patients for at least a minimally independent life in the community after discharge from the hospital. Likewise, social and vocational rehabilitation in the community can significantly improve the quality of life for many long-term severely disabled persons. Having no reason to get up in the morning and no structured day to look forward to are some of the great voids in their lives; for many, rehabilitation can help fill the voids.

There are indications, however, that the mental health treatment system places little emphasis on enhancement of a work orientation, even with patients capable of working (Spivack and others, 1982). Although some patients benefit little from work activities and may not even be able to withstand the pressure they create, they can at least remain relatively asymptomatic in community settings if we meet their dependency needs and do not disapprove of their passivity and inactivity. We should offer them rehabilitation, make it attractive for them, and urge them to participate if they possess sufficient ego strength. But if they do not, and we see them becoming symptomatic or beginning to run from our efforts, we need to come to terms with our own therapeutic ambitions, reduce our pressure on them, and learn how to let them decline such activities gracefully and without fear of censure. If we are to help the psychiatrically disabled realize their full potential, we should maintain high but realistic expectations based on a careful assessment of their ego strength and their ability to handle various kinds of stress.

The great majority of the severely mentally disabled are ignored and are offered few services. Unfortunately, when mental health professionals do turn their attention to the severely disabled, the result is all too frequently a shift from neglect to overenthusiastic attempts at rehabilitation and unrealistic expectations. We run the risk of discrediting rehabilitation if we oversell it and make promises we cannot keep.

A Final Word

Mental health professionals need to accept the fact that there are and will continue to be, given the current state of our knowledge, substantial numbers of the mentally disabled who lack the ego strength needed to make use of rehabilitation efforts; this group can best be helped by supportive management and realistic expectations. Even though we cannot cure, we can do what has too seldom been done down through the ages: make the lives of the long-term severely mentally ill more comfortable.

Our own professional and personal needs, our distaste for dependency and for the lower classes, and our closing ranks with the larger society have led us in the past repeatedly to turn our attention away from severely mentally ill persons. These factors have caused us to neglect—first in the state hospital, now in the community—the long-term mentally ill. Training should be reoriented so that a high priority is given to tolerance of chronic dependency needs and to bridging the gap between the middle-class professional and the lower-class patient. The treatment of the neurotic or personality disorder in uncovering psychotherapy is an interesting and, to many mental health professionals, attractive model. But we must also serve patients who cannot be fitted into this standard model with any expectation of benefit. Moreover, if we provide enough support, including medications, for patients with major mental disorders, they too can learn to use psychotherapy to alter pathological and self-destructive patterns of interaction. We will pursue this issue in Chapter Ten.

The current concern with the plight of the long-term mentally disabled in the community may be again merely a passing phenomenon to be followed by the customary neglect. Since humane supportive care and gratification of dependency needs can keep people in the community and improve the quality or at least the comfort of their lives, then we in whom society has entrusted the care of these citizens must provide it. If our moral disapproval of dependency (often reinforced in our training), our unrealistic expectations of the severely disabled, our disinclination to treat the lower classes, and our tendency to reinforce the antitherapeutic norms of our society prevent us from fulfilling this role, others will take our place and mental health professionals will have demonstrated failure in one of their most important and basic tasks: the care of the long-term, severely mentally ill. A clear understanding of the roots of our neglect and appropriate corrective measures will preserve us from such ignominy.

❧ Three ❧

Deinstitutionalization

Only now is there an acute awareness of what has been an accomplished fact in our society for almost two decades: deinstitutionalization, the mass exodus of psychiatric patients from state hospitals to the community. In 1955 there were 559,000 patients in state hospitals in the United States; today there are approximately 150,000 at any given time (Department of Health and Human Services Steering Committee, 1981). How did such a momentous change come about?

The state hospitals had fulfilled the function for society of keeping the mentally ill out of sight and thus out of mind. Moreover, the controls and structure provided by the state hospital, as well as the granting of asylum, may have been necessary for many of the long-term mentally ill before the advent of modern psychoactive medications. Unfortunately, the ways in which this structure and asylum were achieved and the everyday abuses of state hospital life have left scars on the mental health professions as well as on the patients. The stage had been set for deinstitutionalization by the periodic public outcries about these deplorable conditions, documented by journalists such as Albert Deutsch (1948)—conditions of growing concern too to mental health professionals and their organizational leaders. These concerns led ultimately to the formation of the Joint Commission on Mental Illness and Health (1961), as briefly

Note: Parts of this chapter appeared in an article by the author entitled "What Did We Really Expect from Deinstitutionalization?", *Hospital & Community Psychiatry*, 1980, *32* (2), 105–109.

19

described later in this chapter, and its recommendations for community alternatives to state hospitals.

When the new psychoactive medications appeared (Brill and Patton, 1957; Kris, 1971), along with a new philosophy of social treatment (Greenblatt, 1977), the great majority of the chronic psychotic population was left in an environment that was now clearly unnecessary and even inappropriate for them. Still other factors came into play. First was a conviction that mental patients receive better and more humanitarian treatment in the community than in state hospitals far removed from home. This was a philosophical keystone in the origins of the community mental health movement described later in this chapter. Another powerful motivating force was concern about the civil rights of psychiatric patients; the system of commitment and institutionalization of patients in many ways deprived them of their civil rights. Not the least of the motivating factors was financial. State governments wished to shift some of the fiscal burden for these patients to federal and local government— that is, federal Supplemental Security Income (SSI) and Medicaid and local law enforcement and emergency health and mental health services (Borus, 1981).

The process of deinstitutionalization was considerably accelerated by two significant federal developments in 1963. Under the provisions of categorical Aid to the Disabled (ATD), the mentally ill became eligible for federal financial support in the community; moreover, legislation was passed to facilitate the establishment of community mental health centers. With ATD, psychiatric patients and mental health professionals acting on their behalf now had access to federal grants-in-aid, in some states supplemented by the state, which enabled patients to support themselves or be supported either at home or in such facilities as board-and-care homes (boarding homes) or old hotels at little cost to the state. ATD is now called Supplemental Security Income (SSI) and is administered by the Social Security Administration. Instead of maintaining patients in a state hospital, the states, even those that provide generous ATD supplements, found the cost of maintaining these patients to be far less in the community. Although the amount of money available to patients under ATD was not a princely sum, it was sufficient to pay for a board-and-care home or to maintain a low standard of living elsewhere in the community.

Many private individuals in the community discovered that they could earn substantial additional income by taking former mental patients into their homes even at the rates allowed by the ATD grants. Some private entrepreneurs set up board-and-care homes holding up to or over 100 persons in large old houses and converted apartment buildings and rooming houses (Lamb and Goertzel, 1972a). Although these board-and-care home operators were not skilled in the management of psychiatric patients, they were able to accommodate tens of thousands of persons who had formerly been in state hospitals and who were not now major behavior problems. I will have more to say about board-and-care homes later in this chapter and again, in considerable detail, in Chapter Four.

Another significant federal development came in 1963 when Congress passed the Mental Retardation Facilities and Community Mental Health Centers Construction Act, amended in 1965 to provide grants for the initial costs of staffing newly constructed centers. This legislation was a strong incentive to the development of community programs with the potential to treat people whose main recourse previously had been the state hospital. It is important to note, however, that although rehabilitative services and precare and aftercare services were among the ten services eligible for funding, an agency did not have to offer them in order to qualify for funding as a comprehensive community mental health center.

Also contributing to deinstitutionalization were sweeping changes in the commitment laws of the various states. In California, for instance, the Lanterman-Petris-Short Act of 1968 provided further impetus for the movement of patients out of hospitals. Behind this legislation was a concern for the civil rights of the psychiatric patient. (Much of this concern came from civil rights groups and individuals outside the mental health professions.) The act made the involuntary commitment of psychiatric patients a much more complex process and holding psychiatric patients indefinitely against their will in mental hospitals became a difficult thing to accomplish. Thus the initial stage of what had formerly been the career of the long-term hospitalized patient—namely, an involuntary, indefinite commitment—became a thing of the past (Lamb, Sorkin, and Zusman, 1981).

How many chronically and severely disabled mentally ill persons are there in the United States? Goldman, Gattozzi, and Taube (1981) estimate approximately 1,700,000. They define the chronic population as having severe mental disorder *and* disability that is both severe and prolonged. This number includes 800,000 such persons in the community (of whom 300,000 to 400,000 are in board-and-care facilities). The other 900,000 are in institutions: 150,000 in mental health facilities (including residents for one year or more in state and county hospitals, VA inpatient facilities, private psychiatric hospitals, residential treatment centers, and community mental health center inpatient units) and 750,000 in nursing homes (of whom 400,000 are diagnosed as "senility without psychosis").

What Went Wrong?

In current discussions of deinstitutionalization the question "What went wrong?" is frequently asked (Scherl and Macht, 1979; Halpern and others, 1978). The conditions under which former state hospital patients, and patients who in the past would have become state hospital patients, live in the community have been closely examined, and numerous investigations have uncovered deplorable living conditions. Many also ask why chronically disabled psychiatric patients are not yet in the mainstream of society. Why aren't they being "normalized"? Why hasn't rehabilitation been more successful? Studies have shown that only 10 to 30 percent of former hospital patients have been employed at follow-up and that recidivism has been high: 35 to 50 percent readmitted within one year after hospital discharge and 65 to 75 percent within five years (Anthony, Cohen, and Vitalo, 1978).

Many believe that the problem must be in the service delivery system, which has been shown to be disorganized and chaotic (General Accounting Office, 1978). This belief has led to the argument that most problems of deinstitutionalization could be resolved if there were a concerted effort to improve coordination and integration at the federal, state, and local levels among the various health and social agencies that serve the chronically mentally ill. Another proposed strategy is the development of "model" treatment and re-habilitation programs and their replication on a massive scale. As we will see, it is doubtful whether the complex problems of deinsti-tutionalization have such simple solutions.

In the past decade, society in general and mental health pro-fessionals in particular have moved from one extreme—neglect of the long-term, severely disabled psychiatric patient and a seeming lack of awareness of the impact of deinstitutionalization—to the other extreme—placing a major focus on deinstitutionalization and the long-term patient. Leaders in the field such as John Talbott (1978, 1979, 1981) and Leona Bachrach (1976, 1978, 1979) have been extremely effective in calling attention to the plight of these pa-tients. Apart from the emphasis on deinstitutionalization in the psy-chiatric literature and at mental health conferences, there has been the added glare of publicity from the media. A reordering of priori-ties has been much discussed, and the long-term, severely disabled psychiatric patient has moved from the bottom to the top of the list in just a few years. Thus the climate is such that we currrently have an opportunity that comes along only too rarely: to take effective action to improve the lot of the great majority of long-term patients. But we are in danger of taking only partial advantage of this opportunity.

A major obstacle to understanding and addressing the prob-lems of deinstitutionalization and the long-term patient has been a failure by mental health professionals to recognize that there are many different kinds of long-term patients who vary greatly in their capacity for rehabilitation (see Chapter Fifteen). Patients differ in their ability to cope with stress without decompensating and devel-oping psychotic symptoms. They differ too in the kinds of stress and pressure they can handle; for instance, some who are amenable to social rehabilitation cannot handle the stresses of vocational reha-bilitation and vice versa.

Long-term patients also vary in their motivation to change. Some seem to lack the motivation to function up to their potential because of their need to avoid yet another failure; others, especially the young, may deny the limitations imposed on them by their illness and strive to achieve lofty goals. What may appear to be, at first glance, a homogeneous group turns out to range from people who can tolerate almost no stress at all to people who can, with some assistance, cope with life's demands.

Nevertheless, long-term psychiatric patients constitute, generally, a marginal population. Most controlled studies that compare patients treated in hospitals with those treated in community programs find no significant difference in psychosocial functioning: Low levels are reported for both groups (Test and Stein, 1978). Some pilot studies have shown that modest gains in psychosocial functioning in the community can be achieved through direct and intensive intervention in specific activities of daily living, but these gains are sustained only as long as the treatment continues (Test and Stein, 1978). Paul and Lentz (1977), however, take a more optimistic view. Working with hospitalized patients (as described in Chapter Two), they continued with them after discharge into the community for six months on a declining contact basis. They found that improvement was maintained even after cessation of psychosocial treatment, provided these patients had an adequate social support network (Paul, 1978).

Another important issue, as Shadish and Bootzin (1981) have pointed out, is that the kinds of criteria used in assessing social integration by theorists, researchers, policy makers, and clinicians have a distinct bias in favor of values held by these professionals and by middle-class society generally. Thus, holding a job, increasing one's socialization and relationships with other people, and living independently may be goals that are not shared by a large population of the long-term mentally ill. Likewise, what makes the patient happy may be unrelated to these goals. They may want to avoid the stress of competitive employment, or even sheltered employment, and of living independently. They may experience more anxiety than gratification from the threat of intimacy that accompanies increased involvement with other people. Furthermore, many relatives may be primarily interested in the simple provision of decent custodial care (Thomas, 1980).

Thus for a sizable majority of long-term patients, rehabilitation in terms of competitive employment, high levels of social functioning, and return to the mainstream may not be a realistic goal. Unfortunately, it is the members of this majority who receive the least attention because they cannot achieve lofty goals of rehabilitation and thus disappoint us. We need to realize that if we can simply improve the quality of life for these patients and make them feel comfortable living low-energy but satisfying lives in a nonhospital environment, we will have taken a great step forward in the management of the long-term mentally ill and in making real the benefits expected of deinstitutionalization.

Model Programs: A Solution?

Much attention has been paid to glamorous, innovative, and "successful" pilot treatment and rehabilitation programs with dedicated staff whose enthusiasm is infectious. The publicizing of these programs has led to one proposed remedy for the problems of the deinstitutionalized long-term patient: the mass cloning of these "model programs."

This "solution" demands our scrutiny, for it presents us with serious problems (Bachrach, 1980b). One problem, well described by Mechanic (1978, p. 316), is that even in innovative treatment programs staff find it extremely difficult to maintain the program's early momentum and communicate their enthusiasm to others:

> The conditions they treat are chronic and difficult, and often intractable, and require effective and aggressive services over the long range. In the early stages of any new program there is a sense of excitement and innovation. Both personnel and patients feel that something new is being attempted and accomplished. The energy that comes from such involvement is a very powerful treatment force, but it is difficult to maintain over the long haul. People get tired; they seek to regularize their work patterns; they desire to control the uncertainties and unpredictabilities in their environment. Thus, they tend to push toward the bureaucratization of roles and the clearcut definition of responsibilities and turfs, and they become smug about their own failures, less sensitive to the problems of their clients, and less committed to the jobs that have to be done.

Another problem in replicating the new programs is that what works in one community may not work in another. Some programs are well suited to urban areas but not to rural areas, and vice versa; some programs that work well in small- or medium-sized cities are not feasible in inner-city settings. Even beyond this, programs that are highly successful in one community may fail or be rejected in what appears to be an entirely comparable set of circumstances elsewhere; cultural, political, and socioeconomic factors specific to each community must be taken into account.

Furthermore, it is more exciting to develop and run one's own innovative and pioneering program than to replicate someone else's. Bachrach (1980b, p. 1028) concludes that planners of mental health services have too often looked to "model programs" to provide answers to the problems of deinstitutionalization: "Beyond their demonstration of some very elementary principles of successful programming, model programs tell us only that individual model programs can work. The inductive leap from this position to the notion that because a given model is successful for a specific target population, it can solve the range of problems associated with deinstitutionalization is based on faulty logic; the conclusion does not follow from the evidence at hand."

It is instructive to look at the eight elementary principles common to successful model programs as conceptualized by Bachrach (1980b): (1) assigning top priority to the care of the most severely impaired: (2) realistic linkage with other resources in the community; (3) providing out-of-hospital alternatives for the full range of functions performed in hospital settings; (4) individually tailored treatment for each patient; (5) cultural relevance and specificity, that is, tailoring programs to conform to the local realities of the community in which they are located; (6) trained staff who are attuned to the unique survival problem of chronic mental patients living in noninstitutional settings: (7) access to a complement of hospital beds since there are some patients for whom periods of hospital care continue to be a necessity; and (8) an ongoing internal assessment mechanism that permits continuous self-monitoring.

Some "successful" rehabilitation programs have skimmed the cream of the chronic population in terms of level of functioning and motivation. A few programs have included patients who were only temporarily dysfunctional. When the high employment rates and low recidivism rates achieved by these programs are publicized, others in the field must not infer that such results can be achieved for the chronic population in general—particularly if they expect to include in their own programs all those in need, including the most severely impaired (Bachrach, 1981b). Professionals easily become discouraged when their own efforts fail to measure up to these artificially inflated standards. While it may be appropriate for some special programs to serve a selected group of patients, it must be remembered that mental health systems are responsible for the entire spectrum of long-term patients, from the least to the most disabled.

Is Coordination the Answer?

Many in the mental health field are pursuing still another solution: They are focusing a major share of their energy and resources on finding ways to increase coordination and cooperation between various governmental health, rehabilitation, housing, and income maintenance agencies at the national, state, and local levels. Their aim is to produce a well-integrated system of social and mental health services to replace the disorganized array of agencies, often with overlapping or conflicting goals, that now serve long-term psychiatric patients. These agencies are often reluctant or unable to cooperate with each other because of bureaucratic obstacles or territorial concerns (General Accounting Office, 1978).

Integration of these services would certainly be a vast improvement, but I think we are investing too much in this policy of coordination—especially if our expectation is that it will, in and of itself, lead to a normalized community existence for the long-term patient. There is always the danger of being seduced by the bureaucratic perspective that almost any problem can be solved by making government agencies more efficient and effective. Mega-agencies often respond to pressure with a wealth of promises but only a token effort, leaving the great majority of the target population unserved. By holding out the hope that we can improve conditions for the severely mentally ill at very little added cost, this solution of "fixing" the bureaucracy provides a rationalization for appropriating minimal funds for these chronically underserved patients.

A Philosophical Conflict

A basic conflict within the community mental health movement has contributed to the problems of deinstitutionalization. Perhaps the main reason for the formation of this movement was
concern about the abysmal conditions in large state psychiatric hospitals (Zusman and Lamb, 1977). Community mental health, to the
extent that it grew out of the report by the Joint Commission on
Mental Illness and Health entitled *Action for Mental Health* (1961),
was intended to shrink the populations of large state hospitals by
developing community alternatives and reducing the need for new
admissions. The country was to be covered with community mental
health centers that would provide a wide variety of services to patients normally relegated to state hospitals.

But community mental health in its implementation had a
very different focus. A large proportion of the professionals originally attracted to community mental health were drawn to it by the
prospect of programs that would "prevent mental illness" or focus
on long-term intensive psychotherapy or crisis intervention with
patients who were neither chronically nor severely disabled—that is,
patients with whom the professionals considered it more gratifying
to work (Hogarty, 1971; Stern and Minkoff, 1979).

Efforts at prevention, however, have not in fact reduced the
incidence of major mental illness, the psychoses such as schizophrenia, and the major affective disorders (Lamb and Zusman, 1981). In
the meantime the chronically and severely disabled in the community were given scant attention in terms of direct service. The result
is well described by Bachrach (1978, p. 575): "The deinstitutionalization movement, which was originally designed to provide the
chronically mentally ill relief from the inhumane conditions of institutions, has let these patients 'fall through the cracks.' These
patients—the very ones who have been dehumanized through over-
sight and denial in the past—have somehow, in the process of reducing state hospital populations, largely been lost to the service
delivery system."

It may be possible to retrain community mental health professionals to serve the specific needs of long-term psychiatric patients, but some of these workers may still want to rehabilitate *all*

their patients to try to significantly improve their vocational and social functioning. What if this goal is not feasible for many or most long-term patients? Simply improving the quality of life for these patients and gratifying their dependency needs may be far less than enough for some professionals, especially those whose estimation of their own worth and competence as professionals is determined by their patients' "progress." If community mental health is to succeed in its mission to serve long-term patients, we may well need not only our growing new philosophy and clinical leadership (Stern and Minkoff, 1979) but some turnover of line staff as well.

The insistence of many in community mental health on rehabilitation even when it is not feasible may reflect our feelings of frustration and lack of accomplishment when we cannot transform our patients into independent normal citizens in the community and our society's disapproval of dependency, inactivity, and acceptance of public support (Lamb, 1979a; also see Chapter Two). Yet most of the mentally ill must have extensive emotional and financial support if they are to survive in the community.

The Issue of Liberty

There is often a tendency to underestimate the value and humanizing effects of ex-hospital patients simply having their liberty to the extent that they can handle it (even aside from the fact that it is their right) and of having free movement in the community. It is important to clarify that, even if these patients are unable to provide for their basic needs through employment or to live independently, these are separate issues from that of having one's freedom. Even if they live in mini-institutions in the community, such as board-and-care homes, these are not locked, and the patients generally have free access to community resources.

This issue needs to be qualified. A small proportion of this population needs a highly structured and controlled environment. Furthermore, many of this group refuse help of any kind. For them, simple freedom can result in a life filled with intense anxiety, depression and deprivation, and often a chaotic life on the streets. These persons often need ongoing involuntary treatment, sometimes in 24-hour settings such as locked skilled-nursing facilities (see Chapter Six) or, when more structure is needed, in hospitals where security is greater. Others in need of increased structure and control can live in open settings in the community, such as with family or in board-and-care homes, perhaps with the aid of such mechanisms as conservatorship as is provided in California. (See Chapters Six and Nine for a detailed discussion of conservatorship.) But even those with a structured situation in the community such as conservatorship have varying degrees of freedom and an identity as persons in the community.

Some professionals now talk about sending the entire population of chronically and severely mentally ill patients back to the state hospitals, exaggerating and romanticizing the activities and care the patients are said to have received there. To some, reinstitutionalization seems like a simple solution to the problems of deinstitutionalization (Borus, 1981). But activity and treatment programs geared to the needs of long-term patients can easily be set up in the community, and living conditions can be raised to any level we choose—if adequate funds are made available. In the debate over which is the better treatment setting—the hospital or the community—we must not overlook the patients' feelings of mastery and heightened self-esteem when they are allowed their freedom.

Adequate Living Arrangements

What are the pressing needs of long-term patients living in the community? It cannot be overemphasized that the simple provision of outpatient treatment and rehabilitation, even when daycare five days a week is added, is grossly inadequate for the many long-term patients who need a comprehensive community support system. The key omission is frequently a supportive living situation; without it these patients cannot survive in the community. Chapter Four deals at length with this subject.

Now let us take a brief look at some of the different settings in which nonhospitalized long-term patients live. In California, about half of these patients live with relatives (Lamb and Goertzel, 1977); this figure is higher than is often supposed, since these patients are not as visible as those living in facilities such as board-and-care homes. (In states that have fewer out-of-state patients and thus more families in the state, the proportion of long-term patients living with families is undoubtedly higher.) This situation may be mutually beneficial by providing companionship to both patient and relatives. But it may present serious problems when the relationship is harmful to the patient or family or both (Creer and Wing, 1974; Vaughn and Leff, 1976; Doll, 1976). In this connection, Arnhoff (1975) expresses concern for the effects on children of exposure to psychotic relatives. For a detailed discussion of the issues that arise when long-term, severely disabled patients live with families, see Chapter Eight.

About a third of this population in California lives in board-and-care (boarding) homes (Lamb and Goertzel, 1977)—those products of free enterprise that have sprung up to fill the vacuum created by the emptying out of state hospitals. Although there are serious problems with the extensive use of these facilities, they seem to be here to stay: They house many tens of thousands of patients; they provide a financial return to their operators; and they give many operators a sense of purpose and a feeling of being useful.

In board-and-care homes, patients are provided room and board, varying degrees of supervision and structure, and some treatment, especially in the form of psychotropic medication; these functions are not unlike those of the old custodial state hospital. As we will see in Chapter Four, people in this environment have adjusted to living in the community by what might be called adaptation by decompression; they have found a place of asylum from life's pressures (Lamb, 1979b). Thus for a large proportion of long-term psychiatric patients, the board-and-care home has not only replaced the state hospital as a place to live but has taken over many other functions of the state hospital as well.

Another option for providing community housing to the long-term mentally ill is represented by small innovative programs, many operated by nongovernmental, nonprofit agencies, whose services include living arrangements. Let us take one of the best of the professionally run therapeutic housing programs—satellite housing—as an example (see Chapter Four). Satellite housing may be apartments, duplexes, or small, single-family dwellings. The units are leased by the residents or the mother agency or coleased by both.

Patients live in small groups of two to five, without live-in staff but with some professional supervision.

Satellite housing comes closer than any other therapeutic housing program to helping long-term patients live normal lives in the community. It can probably be more easily adapted to various communities than most model programs; properly run, it can provide quality service and a large measure of integration into the community for many patients. Nevertheless, I have learned from my experience developing two such programs that satellite housing requires a relatively high staff/patient ratio and very competent staff. Even then it works well primarily for the higher-functioning segment of the long-term psychiatric population and only with selected lower-functioning patients; the demands on the severely disabled of even semi-independent living should not be underestimated.

Buttressing the Private Sector

Our examination shows, then, that for a sizable proportion of the long-term mentally ill—those who are unable to live independently and cannot or will not live with relatives—some kind of semi-institutional care is necessary. The private sector has so far filled this need, though not always well. Despite a hail of criticism, do we have a better solution? Do we really want the government to get back into the business of housing many tens of thousands of the long-term mentally ill?

An aspect of this problem that receives too little attention is that Supplemental Security Income (SSI) is often the source of funding for community living situations. If any of us were to try and purchase room, board, and some staff supervision with an SSI grant, what would we get? The answer is obvious—not nearly enough. The need for increased funding for community living arrangements and other community treatment and rehabilitation programs, both public and private, for the chronically mentally ill is, in my opinion, the most pressing issue in mental health today.

I have seen two kinds of arrangements where quality of treatment has been greatly improved in board-and-care homes. In the first kind, local community services have sent professionals and paraprofessionals out to work with each patient in board-and-care homes and to consult with the administrators and staff (see Chapter Five). Such programs, if carried out properly with adequate staff and sufficient outside community programs to which to refer patients, are not cheap; but they can transform a simple residential setting into a therapeutic one (Shadoan, 1976).

In the second kind of arrangement, a mental health professional takes over the facility and hires trained or trainable staff in numbers sufficient to work with each patient living there, individually, in groups and in activity programs. This arrangement supplants the minimal staff supervision normally found in board-and-care homes. The result is often increased stabilization of patients who had previously had a stormy course in the community and, moreover, an increased number of patients in vocational and other community programs. But in the instances I have observed, the cost of such facilities has increased by approximately 100 percent even from the previous California SSI rate (in California the state supplement already doubles the federal SSI rate), and these facilities are now available only to private pay patients.

The private sector, then, properly and effectively monitored by strong licensing agencies, able to charge a reasonable amount, and adequately supported by local mental health and vocational services, can offer cost-effective, high-quality community services on a large scale and with a variety of residential settings (see also Chapters Four and Six). They must be closely monitored to ensure that they meet the needs of a wide range of patients and are tailored to the sociocultural characteristics of their communities. But I cannot emphasize enough that we cannot get the quality of facilities we want or attract the kinds of people we want to operate them if we do not offer sufficient financial incentives.

It is especially important, then, to take action to improve and maintain the quality of facilities such as board-and-care homes and foster homes. This includes supervision of the physical environment and the food and the availability of appropriate treatment and activity programs, both in-house and outside the facilities. Screening out unsuitable foster home sponsors and board-and-care home operators and training the remainder is critical. Essential to this process are strong, effective, well-staffed licensing agencies. Chapter Four discusses this issue at length.

A word about the size of community facilities for long-term patients is in order; in my opinion there is no optimum size. Some patients do best in a small familylike setting where there is considerable interaction with the other residents and the operator of the facility. Others seem to do poorly with too much closeness and nurturing and fare better in a large facility where they can lose themselves and avoid interpersonal contact when they need to.

A Final Word

It is my belief that the lives of the long-term mentally ill in the community can be improved if a variety of community living arrangements, with appropriate treatment and activity programs, are established, supported, and monitored. The private sector can play a major role in this process. This cannot be done on the cheap, however; sizable increases in funding will be needed. The more we are willing to pay per diem for living arrangements and other programs, the more high-quality providers will enter the field and the more our licensing and regulatory agencies can reasonably expect from them. But if we continue to underfund community facilities just as we underfunded the state hospitals, we will continue to provide deplorable conditions for our severely mentally ill and the shame of the states will simply become the shame of the community.

Mental health professionals and society in general must face certain facts if deinstitutionalization is to work for the long-term mentally ill. We must realize that many, and perhaps most, long-term psychiatric patients will never be able to become part of the mainstream of our society. We must also recognize the importance to these patients, in terms of self-esteem, of simply having their liberty. We must rehabilitate those who can be rehabilitated while ensuring that those who cannot will lead lives of dignity and comfort in the community. If we continue to give highest priority to long-term psychiatric patients and do not again lose sight of them as we are drawn to the next glamorous fad in mental health, we can ensure that deinstitutionalization realizes its potential as one of the most positive events in the history of the care and treatment of the mentally ill.

↔ Four ↔

Supportive Community Housing

In my experience, the survival of long-term patients, let alone their rehabilitation, begins with an appropriately supportive and structured living arrangement. Other treatment and rehabilitation are of little avail until patients feel secure and are stabilized in their living situation. As discussed in Chapters Two and Three, deinstitutionalization means granting asylum in the community to a large marginal population, many of whom can cope to only a limited extent with the ordinary demands of life and who have strong dependency needs. Most of the long-term mentally ill need both financial and emotional support—that is, they are dependent on persons or agencies in order to survive in the community. Probably about half of the chronic population in California live with relatives (Lamb and Goertzel, 1977); the proportion is probably higher still in states that have experienced less in-migration and where more long-term patients have families in the state. Thus relatives, with varying degrees of difficulty, provide much of the needed support. Although some of the remaining long-term patients are able to live independently, supportive settings appear necessary for a sizable proportion. There is a wide range of out-of-home living arrangements run as governmental, or as private nonprofit, or as proprietary facilities. Some are transitional in their aims; others are designed to be long-term. It is beyond the scope of this book to describe all these possibilities. For instance, for an excellent exposition of the psychiatric halfway house, see Budson (1978). The purpose of this chapter, then, is to discuss in some depth four kinds of long-term living arrangements in widespread use—board-and-care homes, foster care, the Fair-weather Community Lodge Program, and satellite housing. In the course of this discussion, many of the general issues of housing long-term patients in the community will also be examined. More highly structured settings are discussed in Chapter Six.

Board-and-Care Homes

A recent study in a medium-sized California county showed that approximately one-third of the long-term psychiatric patients in the community younger than sixty-five years of age who were diagnosed as psychotic live in board-and-care (boarding) homes (Lamb and Goertzel, 1977). To what extent are the lives of these patients limited both by their illnesses and by their environment? What is the proper role of board-and-care homes and what should be done to help them maximize the quality of life for their residents and provide a therapeutic milieu?

Board-and-care homes are not the result of careful planning and well-conceived social policy. On the contrary, they sprang up to fill the vacuum created by the rapid and usually haphazard depopu-lation of our state hospitals. Suddenly, many thousands of former state hospital patients needed a place to live and private entrepre-neurs, both large and small, rushed in to provide it.

"Board-and-care home" is used in California to describe a variety of facilities, many of which house large numbers of psychiat-ric patients. The number of residents ranges from one to over a hundred, though according to the state licensing agency the major-ity of patients in Los Angeles are housed in facilities of fifty beds or larger. Board-and-care homes are unlocked and provide a shared room, three meals a day, supervision of medications, and minimal staff supervision.

In my study of a large (110 beds) board-and-care home in Los Angeles (Lamb, 1979b), nine of ten residents had either never tried living alone or had experienced failure the last time they tried. In talking at length with the individuals in this study, there were consistent recountings of an inability to cope with social and vocational demands, an inability to withstand life's pressures, and a paucity of interpersonal relationships. Approximately one tenth of the persons in this study were particularly aware and insightful; they recognized that they became anxious and overwhelmed in social or vocational situations. With varying degrees of reluctance, they had made a conscious decision to limit their exposure to pressure and, in some cases, to avoid pressure of any kind.

The persons in this environment have, therefore, come to what one might call adaptation by decompression. They have found a place of asylum from life's pressures but at the same time a place where there is support, structure, and some treatment, especially in the form of psychoactive medications. For a large proportion of long-term psychiatric patients, the board-and-care home has not only replaced but taken over the functions of the state hospital.

Board-and-care homes provide structure in a variety of ways. Medication management and supervision is one way; psychiatrists come to the facility and prescribe psychoactive drugs for the majority of the residents, and the staff members dispense these medications at regular times. The better members of the staff are reasonably aware of residents who are becoming symptomatic, or more floridly so, and convey this information to the visiting psychiatrists, who may then adjust medications accordingly. Moreover, the staff often sees problems that are causing the resident to become symptomatic and may intervene by manipulating the patient's environment to ease the pressures. In many board-and-care homes the staff supervises the residents' money and disburses it according to their estimate of the resident's ability to handle it. Frequently, the resident is overprotected by this additional structure, but there is flexibility and the staff generally tries to give residents as much responsibility as they can handle. Serving meals at fixed times not only adds structure but ensures that residents will eat properly and regularly. Many residents report that their eating habits were erratic when they lived alone—often to the point of undermining their physical health and certainly their sense of well-being. Although having all their meals prepared may be more than some residents require, most of them have a feeling of being taken care of and of being relieved of a major responsibility.

Despite the protection and structure, board-and-care home residents may have a great deal of freedom. In the facility where my 1979 study was done, for instance, everyone was free to come and go at any hour. Although 5 percent of the residents never leave the building, the other 95 percent use community resources to varying degrees, mostly by visiting local supermarkets and eating places and by taking walks in the neighborhood. Many, of course, probably could and should do more; these patients might well be better stabilized and involved in vocational and other community programs if treatment and rehabilitation were made available within the facility by persons skilled in working with residents with limited ego strength. This lack of staffing, intertwined with problems of funding, has been discussed in Chapter Three and will be further discussed below. But for those who cannot benefit from rehabilitation, an inactive, even reclusive, life-style in a pressureless setting may be the highest level at which they can function for any sustained period of time without decompensation (Murphy, Engelsmann, and Tcheng-Laroche, 1976). It may be correct but misleading to refer to these persons as "regressed" or "institutionalized"; one may be seeing not just the results of their living environment but also the results of their inherent limitations and lack of capabilities.

Although the extensive use of board-and-care homes presents problems, they do serve a need—by housing tens of thousands of patients and providing a return to their operators, both in terms of income and also a sense of purpose and of usefulness. Operators who have no special skills but do possess a home and a desire to feel needed and busy are, in fact, a vast, underutilized resource in our society.

It helps put the issues of board-and-care homes in perspective to note that in the study in California already mentioned (Lamb and Goertzel, 1977), more of the long-term patients in the community younger than age sixty-five were living with families than in board-and-care homes (one half compared to one third). This number is greater than is often supposed, since patients at home are not as highly visible as those living in facilities such as board-and-care homes. Yet the problems at home are equally serious, just not as well publicized. (See Chapter Eight for a discussion of these problems.)

Improving Board-and-Care Homes

It is especially important to take action to improve and maintain the quality of facilities such as board-and-care homes—including adequate financing of them *and* supervision of the physical environment, food, quantity and quality of staff, and whether there are appropriate treatment and activity programs, both in-house and outside these facilities. Screening out unsuitable board-and-care home administrators so that only the competent and ethical are allowed into this field is a critical factor, as is the subsequent training of these persons. Also essential are strong, well-staffed licensing agencies that are both effective and sensitive to the consequences of their actions. Persons working for a licensing agency need to be comfortable in using their authority when required. But first licensing personnel should try to form an alliance with the operators of these facilities so that they work together to improve the patients' living environment and treatment; they should avoid getting into an adversary position with operators unless the operators give them no other choice. If the latter happens, at least some of those operators should be forced out of the field, since if compelled to make changes they do not want to make, some operators may become resentful and in subtle ways take out their resentment on patients.

The issue of funding is critical. Many community living arrangements, including board-and-care homes, are financed by the patient's SSI grant, a small amount compared with Medicaid per diem rates for skilled-nursing facilities, costs of hospitalization, or per diem rates for most community rehabilitation facilities. At these rates, even the most conscientious board-and-care home operator cannot provide the kinds of services that are needed. As described in Chapter Three, increased stabilization in the community and increased involvement in vocational and other community programs can be obtained by providing more services within the facility. This requires greatly enriching facility staffing by increasing the numbers, expertise, and training of staff; it may also mean having the facility run by a mental health professional or having local mental health staff in sufficient numbers who come to the facility and provide a variety of services. The need for increased funding to make these kinds of improvements in community living arrangements, public or private, is obvious.

When one talks with residents and staff and mental health professionals about their experiences with a number of board-and-care homes, a related aspect of this picture often emerges. Some operators are seen as regarding their board-and-care homes almost solely as a business, squeezing excessive profits out of it at the expense of the residents. In many instances, though, the operators are blamed when the fault really lies with society's reluctance to allocate sufficient funding for adequate housing for long-term patients. Having these facilities overseen by a strong licensing and monitoring agency would do much to reassure staff, residents, and outside professionals. Segal and Aviram (1978) suggest that certification of facilities with respect to the quality of the social environment be done by the professionals who place patients in board-and-care homes.

Most patients see themselves as dependent on board-and-care home operators and feel powerless to bring about a higher quality of care. Moreover, many residents are unwilling to organize because they are reluctant to be identified with other mental patients (Segal and Aviram, 1978). Some patients' rights groups have become involved with these issues, but these groups have often *begun* with an adversary stance and have not been sensitive to the patients' problems. Their efforts have too often been not only counterproductive but also destructive to patients. By contrast, the families of the mentally ill have generally been a positive force; they are in most cases sensitive to the problems of long-term patients and supportive of the efforts of those genuinely interested in the care of their relatives (see Chapter Eight). In any event, a balance needs to be struck so that the board-and-care home operators make a fair return on their investment and at the same time provide adequate service to the residents.

There are other problems of board-and-care homes. The importance of cigarettes is striking, and many residents find annoying the constant request to "lend me a cigarette." Drinking frequently gets out of hand, too, and theft is a chronic problem. Competent staff and the fostering of an active resident government appear to reduce but not eradicate these problems for any sustained period of time.

Access to Treatment and Rehabilitation

A "natural experiment" that occurred before my study began provided an opportunity to examine the relationship between distance of a community program and attendance (Lamb, 1979b). For several years, a social rehabilitation program had been run weekly by a well-established, private, nonprofit psychosocial rehabilitation agency. The program was housed in a church about one block from the board-and-care home and operated only during daylight hours. Its range of activities included a coffee hour, bingo, arts and crafts, table games, and literature and poetry discussion groups. Eight months before the study began, the program was moved some distance away, requiring transportation in the board-and-care home's van. One month before the study began, the board-and-care home sold the van for economy reasons.

Sixty-five patients had been in the home long enough to have participated in this experiment. Fifteen patients (23 percent) had never attended the program even when it was a block away. Seventeen patients (26 percent) had attended briefly and stopped because of dissatisfaction with it and/or because of social anxiety. The remaining thirty-three patients (51 percent) stayed with the program. Of these, fourteen (22 percent) stopped when the program moved, even though the van was available to them. Nineteen (29 percent) continued to travel there by van. Seventeen of these patients stopped attending when the van was sold. That left only two patients (3 percent) who were still attending (by bus) at the time of the study.

The experience with the social rehabilitation program at this board-and-care home illustrates the importance of facilitating the residents' use of such programs. Having the program nearby made a crucial difference for the residents who had chosen to use it. Possibly many of those who refused to attend even this program would have participated in a similar program had it been located in the facility. These findings have major implications for mental health planning. Simply enlarging existing clinics and rehabilitation facilities will not reach a large proportion of the board-and-care home population even though it would be a more normalizing experience for them to venture forth and attend a program *outside* the facility. It may well be that long-term patients who function well in community mental health centers and vocational rehabilitation centers are in the minority of the total chronic population, especially when we include all those tucked away in board-and-care homes, living alone, or living with their families.

Goals, Empty Lives, and Contentment

Chronically disabled patients in board-and-care homes have feelings just like anyone else about not having goals, about not being able to reach their goals if they have them, about involutional concerns, about getting old. This holds true not only for those in the involutional group but also for those who are turning thirty and assessing their lives thus far (see Chapter Seven). Many feel that life has no meaning and are distressed by feelings of inadequacy. This may seem self-evident, and yet there is a tendency to forget that long-term patients are affected by the stresses and concerns of each phase of the life cycle. They too have existential concerns just as do we all.

Many are acutely aware of their situations; their lives seem bleak and empty, and they are beset by depression, anxiety, or both. A repeated theme among the residents in my board-and-care home study (Lamb, 1979b) was "I'm just living day by day, waiting for the end." One man referred to being here as "being at the bottom of the dumps." Perhaps some would benefit from better medication management. And surely this group should be the object of a concentrated effort at outreach from community agencies to provide individual and group psychotherapy and social and vocational rehabilitation. But there are those in board-and-care homes, just as there are those in society generally, for whom we do not have the answers with regard to making their lives happy, anxiety-free, and meaningful. Some retreat into fantasy or grandiose delusions to escape from or deny the reality of their lives. This may happen despite medications or because the patient refuses to take them in order to facilitate this escape from reality (Van Putten, Crumpton, and Yale, 1976). Others are too disorganized to be fully aware of reality.

In my study (Lamb, 1979b), more than two fifths of the patients were considered content or reasonably content. Some of these persons probably were not living up to their full potential, and some observers would see their lives as without meaning. For a number of residents, however, the board-and-care home had become an asylum after a lifetime of chaos, instability, and hardship. One 44-year-old schizophrenic man had experienced a lifetime of economic hardship, vocational failure, petty crime, and being in and out of jail and occasionally hospitals before coming to the board-and-care home two years earlier. His feeling of relief was evident; he seemed to have become stabilized and content. A 58-year-old schizophrenic woman had come to the board-and-care home at age 50 after a lifetime of prostitution, living on the streets, and intermittent hospitalization. She talked of a feeling of security she had never before experienced, and she too seemed content.

The lives of a number of persons had in past years been characterized by many psychotic episodes and hospitalizations, each episode further disrupting their sense of psychological integrity and their interpersonal and family relationships. Many appeared to have become stabilized at the board-and-care home; their predominant feeling was a sense of relief. To achieve this feeling of contentment, denial and rationalization were often necessary. One 37-year-old schizophrenic man, a college graduate, had come from an achieving family but had failed at everything he had ever tried. But he had rationalized his life as follows: In his fantasies, he had achieved all his goals one by one. But after achieving them in his fantasies, he found them to be less satisfying than anticipated. There was even a sense of disappointment, he said, after he had realized in his fantasies all his and his family's goals for him; he had anticipated a much greater sense of fulfillment. He knew, therefore, that reaching these goals in real life was not really worth it. And, looking at it this way, he felt reasonably content with his life of reading, taking walks, and keeping up with world affairs.

Those who have experienced board-and-care homes from the inside have stressed the importance of helping these long-term patients keep their respect and dignity (Allen, 1976; Reynolds and Farberow, 1977). Many residents appear reluctant to criticize the board-and-care home or the staff. But some speak freely about both the positives and negatives of the various board-and-care homes where they have lived. It becomes clear that residents are quite sensitive to the way they are treated, both good and bad. To quote one alert and verbal patient who had recently come from a board-and-care home now closed by the state licensing agency, "If you are housed in a dilapidated, poorly maintained building, fed poor-quality food, and treated impersonally by the staff, you cannot help but feel that you aren't worth much, for otherwise you would not be treated that way." It does immeasurable damage to the residents' self-esteem to be served their meals an hour late by kitchen staff, to find no one on the staff who seems to appreciate the importance of the "little things" of everyday living, and to be rebuffed when they make what to them is an important request. For some of the chronically mentally disabled, the board-and-care home or similar facility may be a lifetime residence. Our society has an obligation to provide them services, improve the quality of their lives, and help them gain a sense of self-respect.

Movement In and Out of Board-and-Care Homes

There is evidence that a sizable proportion of the board-and-care home population is not a static group, at least in terms of changing their places of residence (Lamb, 1980a). At six-month follow-up, a third of the residents of the board-and-care home I studied had left. Many have a repeated pattern of leaving to attempt independent living and then returning to the sanctuary of the board-and-care home, either directly or via the hospital. In talking with those who had moved out on their own, what seemed to emerge was a denial of their dependency, a search and yearning for autonomy and a sense of mastery with regard to handling the pressures of living independently.

After varying lengths of time, these residents were again willing to give up their autonomy in exchange for the protection and absence of pressure found in a board-and-care home. After failing in yet another attempt at independent living, they were ready to retreat to a setting where the rewards of life are simple and the demands few. In a board-and-care home, within broad limits, their freedom of movement is unrestricted. In the facility where these studies were carried out, for instance, everyone was free to come and go at any hour. To be sure, living in a board-and-care home presents problems: the constant request for cigarettes from other residents, the frequent theft of one's possessions, the occasional insensitivity of staff. A major problem is the lack, both in quality and quantity, of trained staff. If one is willing to lower one's expectations and can accept a limited environment, however, the board-and-care home can provide asylum for those who lack the ego strength to handle more than a passive, inactive life-style. The basic needs of life are provided for, the pressures are few, other people are available for whatever level of socialization the resident wants and can tolerate, and tolerance for unusual behavior is greater here than in the mainstream of life.

Many residents move from one board-and-care home to another. Most of them say that another board-and-care home will solve their problems—such as being influenced to drink by friends, feeling bored and depressed, feeling they have no friends, or simply a general dissatisfaction with life. While there are valid reasons for the move in some cases (such as wanting to try a smaller facility with a familylike setting to see if this would improve their functioning or quality of life), in other cases it appears to be an attempt at a geographical solution to what is in fact the resident's internal problem.

The great majority of board-and-care home residents who move on do so within the first year (Lamb, 1980a). In the board-and-care home where these studies were done, over two fifths of the residents had been there five years or more. As several residents put it, "The longer you stay here, the harder it is to leave." Perhaps many of those who move on are trying to escape the pull of dependency and avoid the feelings of despondency they get when they leave behind the newcomer phase in a board-and-care home, begin to look around at their fellow residents, and begin to feel they will never leave (Reynolds and Farberow, 1977). Those who move on tend to be younger and perhaps not yet ready to give in to this pull of dependency and come to terms with living in a sheltered, segregated, low-pressure environment.

Those who move on are more apt to have been hospitalized during the preceding year, to be younger, and still to have life goals (Lamb,1980a); some residents of the board-and-care home may regard leaving the comparatively static milieu of the home as a necessary step in realizing their goals. Such a struggle for achievement or to make life changes may take its toll in more frequent crises and hospitalization.

Those who remain in board-and-care homes for extended periods of time tend to be older, to have fewer goals for themselves, and to have been hospitalized less within the preceding year. This group appears to have settled into the routine of board-and-care life, given up whatever earlier goals they may have had, and settled for a more limited existence. Using hospitalization as the criterion, they have stabilized to a greater degree. Having "weighed" the costs of striving for independence and achievement against lowering their goals or even giving up, which poses less risk of failure, stress, and decompensation, they seem to have surrendered to the pull of dependency.

Interaction with Family

Ambivalence about living with their families is prominent among many residents when they discuss their feelings and attitudes toward their relatives. Families also seem ambivalent toward residents. This ambivalence is probably in large part responsible for many residents living apart from their families even though both may express a desire to live together again. A tenth of the residents in the board-and-care home I studied had a pattern of shuttling between family and board-and-care home (Lamb, 1979b); more than a fifth of those who had left at six-month follow-up had returned to their families. It appeared that the residents exceeded the family's tolerance in a variety of ways; but after a period of respite from each other, while the resident was living in the board-and-care home, both the resident and family were willing to try living together again.

In another 8 percent of the study group, the patient's board-and-care home placement had come about immediately after an episode of violence. In half these cases, there had been no contact with the family since the incident, even though at least five years had passed; in the other half, contact between patient and family was maintained. In these latter cases, it seemed that living in the board-and-care home placed enough distance between the patient and the family that further contact now seemed safe. About one fifth of the residents seemed to have exceeded, in a variety of ways other than violence, the family's tolerance of them on a full-time basis; but with the relationship diluted by the patient living in the board-and-care home, there continued to be regular contact between these residents and their families over long periods of time.

In some cases, aging parents seemed unable to deal with or take care of the patient any longer. Their tolerance of their offspring's behavior appeared to have diminished with their advancing age. Six percent of the residents appeared to have done well at home throughout their lives until the mother (or, in one case, the grandmother) died. With the absence of the maternal figure, the remaining family members seemed unable or unwilling to have the resident at home.

Structure

The concept of structure is important in determining each patient's housing needs. While most patients need only a moderate amount, others need a highly structured environment to compensate for their lack of internal controls and give them the sense of security they need. Structure is provided by a high staff/patient ratio as opposed to minimal staff supervision, by the dispensing of medication by staff (who may or may not be licensed depending upon the state and the type of facility) as opposed to patients taking their own medication, by establishing curfews as opposed to letting patients come and go as they please, by offering therapeutic activities that may structure most of the patients' day as opposed to letting patients spend their time as they choose, by giving patients little voice in the running of the facility as opposed to allowing them almost complete self-direction through such mechanisms as house governments (Fairweather, 1980), and by providing a locked setting as opposed to an open one. How much structure does a patient need? The answer depends on the individual patient. The professional responsible for the case needs to decide whether a particular facility has too much, the appropriate amount, or not enough structure to meet the needs of each patient.

That a patient may need considerable structure is neither good nor bad; it is simply a clinical decision. Many long-term, severely disabled psychiatric patients need little, if any, structure. Others, however, lack sufficient impulse control to cope with an open setting such as a board-and-care home or with family. They need a high degree of external structure and control on an ongoing basis to compensate for the inadequacy of their own internal controls. The number of such patients may not be great when compared to the entire population of severely disabled patients. If placed in the community in living arrangements without sufficient structure, however, this group can disrupt the community and take up an inordinate proportion of the time of mental health professionals, let alone other agencies such as the police, welfare, parks, and libraries. More important, they may constitute a danger to themselves or others. It is clinically useful to remember that not all problems can be solved in an open, relatively unstructured setting; sometimes the best solution is to transfer a patient to a more structured setting. Many of those who fail in board-and-care homes (as measured by stabilization in the community) are in need of more structure than a board-and-care home can provide. Chapter Six offers a detailed discussion of these issues.

Foster Care

A foster home is defined as care in a small family setting. According to Linn (1981), small means five or fewer patients in a family home. The prototype of foster care is that of Geel, a town in Belgium where mental patients have been cared for in the homes of its townspeople for over seven hundred years. In Geel, homes are still limited to one or two patients and patients are seen as an integral part of society and especially of the family. Patients have a bedroom of their own that facilitates privacy. They share their meals and leisure activities with the family and participate, though less today than in the past, in the family's domestic and income-producing work, thereby supplementing the modest payments for their care made by the state (Srole, 1977). Cuvelier (1975) describes foster care in Geel as a process in which the patient arrives rootless and homeless and then experiences a family in a normal home. The patient participates in daily home activities, is expected to behave well, and gradually becomes a family member in the sense of forming affective bonds as he or she learns to adapt to the reality demands of the family. Thus the patient assumes a family role. In the United States the greatest use of this arrangement has been made by the Veterans Administration, which has about 11,000 psychiatric patients in foster care (Linn, 1981).

Linn, Klett, and Caffey (1980) describe three characteristics of foster homes associated with improvement in social functioning: more children in the home; fewer fellow patients in the home; and size of the home in terms of fewer total occupants. Specifically with regard to schizophrenics, more activity in the home (higher degree of sponsor-initiated leisure activities) and more intense supervision were associated with deterioration in social adjustment. This finding is consistent with observations already discussed in Chapter Two—that schizophrenics become symptomatic when they are unable to withdraw from too much social stimulation (Wing, 1977). It is also consistent with my own observations that many schizophrenics do poorly in small homes where there is much nurturing and closeness and gravitate toward larger facilities where they can withdraw when they need to and limit their interpersonal interaction.

Foster care operators tend to be understandably particular about whom they will take into their homes and live with. It is one thing to deal with a hostile paranoid patient or one with distasteful personal habits on an eight-hour shift; it is something else to live with that person twenty-four hours a day. Thus, despite the appeal of "family living," foster care is not the living arrangement of choice for many long-term patients. Nevertheless, the experience of the Veterans Administration, the lessons of Geel, and my own observations in many small homes indicate that foster care can be an important resource for a large population of long-term psychiatric patients and is greatly underutilized in the United States.

Fairweather's Sheltered Subsociety

Fairweather and others (1964, 1969), recognizing the need of the chronic mentally ill for support in many aspects of their lives, developed a sheltered subsociety in the community to meet the housing and social as well as vocational needs of these patients. Carefully designed evaluation was built into each phase of his program. Since there was a control group for each group of patients being exposed to his experimental programs and sophisticated statistical analysis was employed, it is possible to evaluate all aspects of his program. From a research point of view Fairweather's program has been a model for experimental social innovation.

Fairweather began by establishing in the hospital a program based on the use of small problem-solving groups. It was found that these small groups of patients whose daily activities were organized around solving their own problems could be effective even when composed of the most chronic patients. To complete this program successfully, each patient had to progress through four steps of increasing responsibility and rewards—that is, money and passes outside the hospital. The small group was responsible, as a unit, for each individual's progress through these steps. Although the program did get patients out of the hospital sooner, the readmission rate was as high for these patients as for those in the control group, who had been exposed to the traditional treatment program of the hospital. The crucial factor in remaining in the community was found to be the amount of support the patient received from the people with whom he or she lived. When these facts had become clear, Fairweather's group decided to move these problem-solving patient groups as units from the hospital to the community.

This new phase of the program involved setting up the Community Lodge program: a dormitory for patients and a sheltered work situation—a janitorial service owned and operated by the ex-patients themselves. Initially those in the Community Lodge program needed considerable supervision, but they eventually were able to handle most of their problems themselves. Medical care was provided by a private physician in the community. All of the ex-patients' customary daily needs, such as food preparation, were managed by the group itself. Eventually these ex-mental patients became almost entirely autonomous and self-supporting. The increase in the number of patients in the Community Lodge program who were able to remain in the community was striking compared with patients in the control group who were receiving traditional community services. Furthermore, all patients in the Community Lodge program were employed—either in the janitorial service or in the basic functions of the lodge such as meal preparation. But reduction in recidivism and increased employment were not the only benefits. The members of the lodge also had strong feelings of pride about the organization, themselves, and their accomplishments.

Fairweather notes a number of points that are crucial to the success of his program. First, a high degree of ego involvement must be developed by the participants in order to make the subsociety work. The task performed by the members must be meaningful and important to them. The feeling of identification with the success of the organization is enhanced by the patient's ownership of the business. Further, the subsociety must give as much autonomy as possible to its members consistent with their behavior.

Fairweather stresses that leaders must emerge from the patient group itself. In this regard, he found that a heterogeneous group composed of both socially active and passive members creates a social climate that encourages leaders to emerge. Homogeneous composition of all socially active or all passive, inactive members produces intergroup conflict in the former case and stagnation in the latter.

Maximum efforts are made to organize this newly created social system in such a way that the patients' social status depends not on their psychopathology but on what they can achieve with the unimpaired portions of their ego-functioning. Within the subsociety there is a vertical organization so that a division of labor is possible and also a meaningful role can be found for all members. Thus, if upward mobility is permitted, capable and motivated members can achieve higher social status (such as crew leader for the janitorial service). At the same time a meaningful social position is available to members who are not capable of higher social positions or do not aspire to them within the organization. If a diversity of work is provided within the subsystem, it is more likely that work that has meaning for every member can be found. Thus in the lodge program there are jobs within the lodge, such as the kitchen crew and the bookkeeper, and jobs in the janitorial business. Within these jobs are different work statuses: foreman and worker. Even within the worker category it is possible to reward the ex-patients monetarily according to their productivity, marginal workers getting less than the more productive ones.

Fairweather also stresses the establishment of internal norms that are tolerant of deviant behavior. At the same time, the group must make it clear to members that deviant behavior must be limited as much as possible to the subsystem and must not be manifest in the community at large. Thus, the group may tell a patient that it is acceptable to hallucinate in the lodge, or in the truck going to or from work, but conversing with hallucinated voices is not permitted out on the job.

Sociologically, this sheltered subsociety gives the chronic patient a social role in the community that is not labeled and stigmatized as deviant; it provides sufficient social distance from community agents of social control so that the chronic deviant's rule-breaking behavior becomes less visible to the community at large. Thus, behavior can be controlled and regulated within the framework of the subsociety itself, where there is greater understanding of the problems and where there are therapeutic ways of dealing with them. While social controls are stressed, there is also emphasis on setting up a system that ensures that the patients continue to take their medications. Fairweather does not see his lodge program as transitional. It is a permanent subsociety. He believes that, even when patients make a good adjustment in his community program, few would be able to remain in the community if they left the supportive environment of the program.

The Community Lodge program has been replicated throughout the United States and in foreign countries; various aspects have been adapted to meet cultural, political, and socioeconomic factors specific to each community (Fairweather, 1980). Its dissemination, however, has not been as great as had been hoped; perhaps that has to do with the problems inherent in model programs (see Chapter Three). In any case Fairweather's work stands as a landmark in the community treatment of the long-term mentally ill.

Satellite Housing

No therapeutic housing program comes closer to helping long-term patients live normal lives in the community than satellite housing. Satellite housing offers patients, with the aid of the satellite housing staff, a life-style they could not otherwise attain or maintain because of their illness—a life-style with freedom, considerable independence, integration into the community, and a sense of dignity. Satellite housing may be apartments, duplexes, or small, single-family dwellings. The housing is leased by the residents or the mother agency or coleased by both. Here patients live in small groups of two to five without live-in staff but with professional supervision. Satellite housing is especially suited for patients who cannot quite survive in an independent living arrangement but do not require the support and structure of a board-and-care home or foster home. Satellite housing is an extremely attractive concept, but it should be emphasized that it is not for everyone. Whether or not a patient is ready to handle this degree of independence must be carefully assessed for each individual if we are not to set patients up for painful failures. The demands on the severely disabled posed by even semi-independent living should not be underestimated.

In satellite housing, shopping, cooking, and housework are shared, and residents have a responsibility for paying the rent (either to the landlord directly or to the agency). Staff members assigned to satellite housing programs are available as needed for guidance and counseling, both individual and group, and are also on call around the clock for emergencies. In a typical satellite housing program, residents of three or four apartments form a stable group of regular meetings, sometimes with staff and sometimes without. These group meetings are hosted by the residents within their own housing units on a rotating basis.

Sometimes a "satellite apartment program" is simply an apartment house in which most of the apartments are occupied by patients. In my opinion this is not really satellite housing; satellite housing programs should not involve more than one or two apartments in any one building and the apartments should be scattered about the community if we are to achieve our goal of integrating patients into the community.

Acquisition by a satellite housing program of a large number of community apartments increases the possibility that roommates can be matched in terms of age, personality, interests, and level of functioning. Generally, apartments of four persons work out better than apartments housing only two. With four persons in a unit there is more peer support when one of the patients is not doing well or is in crisis. The larger group also means that patients can withdraw when they need to limit their interpersonal interaction, a situation that could easily leave a single roommate feeling alone, unsupported, and rejected.

Satellite housing programs often have a higher-expectation philosophy—that is, residents are expected to have a meaningful daytime activity outside of the house in addition to helping with the chores at home. This requirement should be flexible. Many residents comfortably spend their days in short-term day treatment centers, vocational rehabilitation programs, or competitive employment. But some patients, otherwise entirely suited for satellite housing, will only be able to deal with a low-key social activity center a few hours a week. Still others may find the requirement for an outside activity of any kind more than they can handle, at least at first. One should avoid hasty decisions to shift these patients to facilities such as board-and-care homes. A satellite unit can be organized on a family model; some residents may have an outside daytime activity while others remain at home, perhaps taking responsibility for cooking the meals and cleaning the house. Simply living in the unstructured setting of a satellite apartment, with only a few responsibilities, is the limit of many patients' capabilities. Asking only this much of such patients is for them high expectations.

Ideally, staff intervention will also be flexible. The fragile, fearful resident with a limited anxiety tolerance needs more staff support than other residents. A period of close contact between staff and resident, apartment mates, and therapist may often head off a crisis that might lead to rehospitalization. Occasionally, the resident will have to be removed from the apartment and placed for a brief period in a halfway house or community crisis house or local hospital.

Who has primary responsibility for the patient in satellite housing? This question is an important one. There is merit in the satellite housing requirement that each patient have a primary therapist who deals with the main issues in the patient's life as well as crises. Otherwise the satellite housing staff can easily find itself in the role of primary therapist for most of the patients and responsible for all aspects of their lives. This responsibility reduces the time and energy the staff can devote to their primary task: the housing program.

There should be a willingness to decrease services as well as increase them. Some satellite residents can stabilize at a level where staff intervention or supervision is needed only occasionally. At this point, the residents have made a normal adjustment to the community and the goal of integration into the community has been met.

A Final Word

If we are to truly improve life for the long-term psychiatric patient in the community, we will need the allocation of sizable increases in public funding to establish, support, and monitor a variety of community living arrangements, with varying degrees of support and structure, as well as high-quality treatment and activity programs. In my experience, community treatment and rehabilitation is not effective unless these patients are stabilized in appropriately supportive and structured living arrangements. Adequate funding and monitoring will also ensure the continuing quality of these living arrangements. Our strategy, then, should be to improve what we have, as for instance board-and-care homes, and expand such arrangements as foster care, Community Lodge programs, and satellite housing.

❧ Five ❧

Consultation to Residential Care Facilities

In the early years of the community mental health movement most professionals were caught up in a pioneering spirit of enthusiasm. There seemed to be no bounds to what community mental health could accomplish, and the principles of preventive mental health were widely accepted because they suited the prevailing optimism. Mental health consultation was endorsed as an exciting new means of primary prevention: the actual prevention of cases of mental disorder (Lamb and Zusman, 1981). It seemed only common sense to intercept people at risk before they became psychiatric casualties and patients in the mental health service delivery system. Offering consultation to non-mental health human service agencies seemed an eminently logical way to reach, if indirectly, a great number of potential psychiatric patients with a minimum expenditure of energy and funds. Although many of those receiving mental health consultation in the schools, in welfare agencies, in police departments, and in other community agencies have been pleased and feel they have benefited from it, there is little evidence that one of the

Note: This chapter is a revised version of a paper by the author and Carolyn L. Peterson entitled "The New Community Consultation," *Hospital & Community Psychiatry,* in press.

basic premises of preventive mental health has been proved—that this consultation has in fact had an impact on the persons served by these agencies in terms of actually preventing diagnosable mental disorder.

In the past decade other far-reaching changes have taken place. There has been a shift back to the original aims of community mental health—namely, giving a high or even the highest priority to the chronically and severely mentally ill (Zusman and Lamb, 1977). And since a large number of the chronically mentally ill live in nonmedical community residential facilities run by administrators and staff not specifically trained in managing problems of psychiatric patients, mental health consultation to residential facilities has become an issue of high priority. It should be emphasized that this kind of consultation is not really primary prevention but secondary and tertiary prevention—that is, part of the treatment and rehabilitation of these patients. Thus, freed from the shackles of ideology, namely having to see consultation as actually preventing mental illness, mental health professionals can see this consultation for what it is: a much needed and powerful treatment strategy in the mental health delivery system for long-term patients in the community.

Consultation to staff can enhance the treatment in the full range of residential facilities—halfway houses, board-and-care homes, nursing homes, and locked structured community facilities. In many of these facilities, such as board-and-care homes, most staff are not professionals. Consultation to these facilities will be the focus of the chapter. While one can learn by trial and error how to deal with psychiatric patients, my colleague and I have seen the process greatly facilitated by consultation from a skilled professional. Sometimes the most elementary principles of patient treatment and management can come as a revelation to nonprofessional staff. For example, nothing is more difficult for some staff than feeling comfortable in being direct with patients and setting limits on inappropriate behavior and unreasonable demands. The untrained staff member may assume that the mentally ill are exceptionally fragile and that saying no to them will cause them to fall apart. The staff member may become anxious and ask, "What should I do? I don't want to hurt him." Here the consultant's role is to encourage staff to feel free to say no to a patient's inappropriate requests—for example, asking for personal information about a staff member or wanting to borrow money—and to stop other inappropriate or disruptive behavior, such as interrupting conversations, stealing, or spending all one's monthly personal money in a day. Not only does saying no frequently lead to appropriate behavior but it also helps patients in terms of improving their reality testing and their sense of what is socially acceptable. Even simple consultation like this can make the difference between a therapeutic and nontherapeutic facility.

This chapter reviews some of the knowledge that a mental health consultant can convey to nonprofessional staff to help them work more effectively and therapeutically with long-term patients in residential and rehabilitation settings. But first I explain what the consultant needs to know and understand about the new community settings and his or her relationship with the staff who work in them.

What Consultants Need to Know

Residential community care facilities have to contend with changing licensing regulations, zoning problems, rapid staff turnover, referral inequities, and tenuous neighborhood relationships—considerations quite different from problems usually found in the milieu of the mental health professional. Administrators of residential facilities often criticize consultants in the following terms (Eisdorfer and Batton, 1972; Peterson, 1976): "He doesn't really know how the facility operates and thus what our priorities are." "She doesn't know us as individuals and has no idea of what our responsibilities and time pressures are." "His values and needs might make him less sensitive to our values and needs." "Who is she to criticize my operation when she's never had to shoulder this responsibility herself?"

Consultants thus need to familiarize themselves thoroughly with the consultee's job and demonstrate that they value and understand the consultee's tasks. The effect on their rapport will be inestimable. The consultant may begin the consultation relationship by saying, "I don't really understand your job yet. Would you tell me more about it so that I can help you?" Following this admission by the consultant, consultees feel less defensive and much more free to express, identify, and clarify their needs (Jarvis and Nelson, 1967).

A consultant to a residential community care facility, then, should become familiar with a host of issues: recent licensing evaluation reports on the facility and documents, structural safeguards, and resocialization activities necessary to satisfy the licensing authority; food storage and preparation provisions, and an assessment of the atmosphere in which meals are served; staffing patterns, including who does what and when; existing relationships with referral agencies, orientation procedures for new residents, and information received about their continuing treatment needs; emergency procedures; available and utilized community resources in the neighborhood; administration and storage of drugs; and the administrator's background, training, and previous work experience (Peterson, 1979).

The facility should assist people in their social reintegration when they have become able to maintain themselves in the community and after their disturbing symptoms have been controlled. David Reynolds, who described community care from the inside after posing as a resident, claims that many board-and-care homes are not bad places to live but they are very limiting (Reynolds and Farberow, 1977). Consultants should learn what limitations are inherent in the residential situation, what expectations are realistic in terms of funding and the training and expertise of administrator and staff, and what available resources may improve the quality of care. They should understand that they are no longer on their own turf and that acceptance of the characteristics of this nonmedical setting will allow them to exert a beneficial effect on facility staff and residents.

It is important that the consultant recognize that residential care administrators often see themselves as being looked down on by mental health professionals (frequently a correct perception). They fear their opinions will be ignored. They feel that mental health professionals, licensing agencies, and the politicians who determine the level of reimbursement and just about anyone else "think I am only in it for the money and anything I say is just self-interest."

In truth, alternative community resources were not created by the public sector with the same vigor as deinstitutionalization was pursued. (See also Chapters Three and Four.) Programs and funds were inadequate to deal with the difficulties that formerly institutionalized psychiatric patients would have in adjusting to community life. There was little preparation for changing the dependent passive role expected of former patients in the hospital setting to the more independent responsible role expected of the citizen in the community. Often, all that was accomplished was the transfer of persons from the mental health budget to the welfare budget (Reich and Siegel, 1973).

Criticism of the large numbers of proprietary facilities that responded to the growing need for care of the mentally ill in the community led eventually to tighter controls. But new requirements—setting treatment goals for individuals, providing activity programs, promoting rehabilitation—have seldom been supported by additional revenue or training for facility staff. Nor has a generally accepted procedure been developed for professional support or supervision of community care facilities. Case management legislation has not been successful in attracting enough mental health professionals to work with long-term patients, let alone providers who are responsible for their care. Therefore administrators of community care facilities still feel left out of the mental health service delivery system and unclear about how to meet the new expectations.

Given these realities of the community setting, the consultant needs to know how patients can take advantage of the opportunities (and minimize the limitations) that the community has to offer before he or she can relay this information to the facility staff. Most long-term severely disabled patients have a need for asylum to a greater or lesser degree (Lamb, 1979b). Some may be able to live comfortably in a satellite housing program (apartments or small houses with some supervision but no live-in staff) that approaches independent living; others may need a low-pressure board-and-care home where most of their needs are met. The consultant should see that neither of these possibilities, or any of the possibilities in between, is good or bad per se. The important thing is to realize that patients should not be expected to do more than they are able—but, at the same time, nothing should be done for them that they can do for themselves (Test and Stein, 1977). It should also be understood that long-term patients vary greatly in their capabilities and their needs in the various areas of their lives—social, vocational, interpersonal, living arrangements—and they may fall at one end of the spectrum between independence and dependence in one area of their lives and at the other end of the spectrum in another area (see Chapter Fifteen).

The consultant should also recognize that patients should be presented with the full range of treatment and rehabilitation opportunities available to them. Further, they need to be informed of the appropriate behavior required by whatever role they desire in the community (Wolkon, 1970). If a patient wishes to attend a sheltered workshop, he should know that this will entail arising at a regular time each morning, securing a bus pass, keeping his clothing clean and presentable, getting along with others, maintaining regular attendance, and performing the duties he is assigned. Assignment to a workshop will then provide him with opportunities to learn the needed skills of the new role and test his ability to move toward at least a limited level of independence.

Further, by recognizing that the mental patient returning to the community probably suffers from impaired functioning in social roles, the consultant can help nonprofessional staff provide support during the crisis of role transition (Wolkon, 1974), anticipatory guidance about what is expected of patients in various community situations, and training in appropriate social skills.

It is also essential that the consultant keep in mind the concept of structure. While most patients need only a small to moderate amount, others need a highly structured environment. Structure has already been mentioned in Chapter Four and will be discussed further in Chapter Six. The consultant to a facility with an open setting should realize that not all problems can be solved in that setting and that sometimes the most helpful solution is to transfer a patient to a more structured setting. These patients need not necessarily be sent to state hospitals, however. An alternative in California is the locked skilled-nursing facility with special programs for the mentally ill; an intensive program that schedules most of the patient's day is a key element in providing structure. This program gives patients a chance at treatment and rehabilitation in a structured setting in their home community (see Chapter Six). Consultants to such facilities should remember that close monitoring of these patients is essential if they are to be transferred to a less restrictive setting as soon as possible.

What Consultants Need to Convey

Consultation is an interaction between at least two persons in which the consultant helps the consultee with a work problem in an area where the consultant has special competence. In this case the problem relates to the management and treatment of patients or to the planning and implementation of programs on behalf of patients (Caplan, 1970). We have seen that the consultant should acquire understanding of and expertise about the community setting and the deinstitutionalized patient if the consultant is to become competent to offer mental health consultation. The consultant needs to be clear, however, that the ultimate goal is to encourage the consultee to deal with work problems independently in the future. Further, while many care providers tend to expect the consultant to help by "making the problem go away," the consultant should emphasize the collaborative nature of a consultation relationship in which the consultee is free to accept or reject advice and is willing to accept responsibility for taking action (Davis and Peterson, in press).

By asking questions, sharing his own experiences, and modeling, the consultant can help care providers gain a sense of mastery over their own work situations. In some cases, this aid may entail providing direct services to the consultee's patients, although it is not recommended that a new consultant wear two hats in terms of providing both consultation and direct services. The goal for all direct-service delivery should be modeling therapeutic interaction as opposed to "doing for" the consultee. It has been my experience that the development of a collaborative relationship with care providers poses special problems if the consultant also has a commitment to preserve the confidentiality of therapeutic relationships with patients at the facility. Moreover, it is hard to learn the complex process of consultation when one is at the same time immersed in the responsibilities of direct patient care. So, at best in such a situation where the consultant has an ongoing direct-service commitment to the facility, the consultation should be limited to as short a time as possible.

Just as there are common problems encountered in community care facilities, there are common solutions that have become part of the body of knowledge of consultation in recent years. The following paragraphs describe some of the problems that consultants may encounter and offer suggestions for what the consultant should convey.

Determining *admission criteria* is one of the basic problems and an important first step. The mental health delivery system should aim to serve the full range of patients. Of course each facility can only serve a certain group. But that group needs to be specified, and the facility staff should know what they are trying to accomplish and with whom. Some facilities admit only patients at the higher functioning end of the spectrum—that is, those patients who can participate in vocational rehabilitation activities and who are eager or at least willing to pursue treatment recommendations, such as day treatment, outpatient psychotherapy and medication, and social rehabilitation. Other facilities focus on patients at the lower end of the spectrum in terms of potential and motivation for treatment and rehabilitation. This task should not be relegated to a low-status function; both the consultant and the consultees need to see the importance of caring for and improving the quality of life of the many long-term psychiatric patients who function at the lower end of the scale. It may well be that this latter group far outnumbers the former.

The consultant can play a key role in facilitating the establishment of *house government*. The facility administrator often needs assistance in determining the level of responsibility that can be handled by the particular group of patients in his or her facility; the administrator also needs support when it comes to delegating to the patients what were formerly the administrator's responsibilities, prerogatives, and matters under his control (Peterson, 1979).

A characteristic found to a greater or lesser extent in almost all chronic schizophrenics is *difficulty in tolerating closeness and intimacy*. Often the consultant will need to point this out. While some patients thrive on a large dose of nurturing and closeness from care givers and fellow patients, others are driven back to the hospital by it. If the facility staff understands this, they will be able to interact with patients in accordance with their needs. Sometimes it will be decided that the patient is in the wrong facility—that he or she should be moved to a smaller, more nurturing facility or conversely to a larger one where it is easier for the patient to "have his space." As the reader may have already gathered, a wide variety of residential facilities, in terms of size and style of management, are needed to serve the chronically mentally ill.

The importance of *setting limits* has already been discussed. It is essential to stress to the facility administrator and staff that setting limits on the patient's behavior is needed not simply to meet the needs of the facility in terms of what it can tolerate; it is also a crucial ingredient of treatment for many long-term patients. Thus, it needs to be understood that limits may be a key factor in helping the patient.

The consultant can help facility operators and staff *understand the mental health system.* This does not mean complete understanding of community mental health programs but knowledge of what a day treatment center is, what a sheltered workshop is, what a mental health clinic does, and how one manages to gain admission to these facilities. For many patients, these facilities comprise a large part of their world, and the staff needs to know what patients are talking about. Staff should also know when a referral is indicated and how to arrange for it, either by talking to the patient's therapist or by making the referral directly if need be.

Crisis management may not usually be the primary responsibility of the facility operator and staff, but they should understand what can precipitate crises. They should be looking for precipitating stresses that may thrust a person already predisposed to psychosis into a frank psychosis. Such stresses include changes in one's work or vocational rehabilitation status, problems with relationships (breaking up with a person of the opposite (or same) sex or getting too intimate with another person), or not knowing what behavior is expected in a new role, including admission to a community facility. All this may seem obvious to mental health professionals, but it may not be self-evident to the untrained.

The problem of *alcohol and drugs* can be a thorny one. Should one allow patients to drink socially in the facility or should there be complete prohibition? Experience has taught me that allowing "social drinking" works only rarely, for the theoretical line between social drinking and problem drinking is hard to draw in practice. It seems more effective to have a policy of no drinking or drug use in the facility and to stipulate that no one may return to the facility under the influence of alcohol or drugs. Obviously, one will rarely achieve a situation where alcohol and drug use will be totally eliminated, but such a policy is clear and, I think, least subject to manipulation. If consistently implemented, it enables the facility operator and staff to maintain the amount of control and sobriety necessary for a therapeutic milieu. If some patients will not or cannot go along with the policy and create problems for the facility with their drinking and drug use, the operator and staff should be encouraged to ask such persons to leave.

Perhaps no problem is more difficult than that of helping the staff deal with *antisocial personality disorders* (Lamb and Odenheimer, 1969). Generally these cases are people who tend to act out or live out their problems rather than internalizing. Close, meaningful relationships are extremely threatening to them; as they become involved with staff and other patients, they tend to revert to some of their antisocial and acting out behavior, character defenses that can serve to ward off the threat of intimacy. Thus, disruptive behavior, excessive drinking, undermining of staff and patients, and the like become obstacles not only to their own treatment but to the treatment of the total patient group. Moreover, schizophrenic patients with poor ego strength are impressed by the charm and what seems like the relatively healthy ego strength of the sociopath and are easily influenced by the patient who uses sociopathic defenses. Sometimes psychotic patients with poor ego strength and poorly fixed identities are manipulated into acting out for sociopathic patients while the latter sit "innocently" in the background. Moreover, schizophrenic patients are often frightened by the sociopath's lack of impulse control and become even more frightened when the staff seems unable to cope with it. Conversely, the schizophrenic who is unable to rebel himself may vicariously enjoy watching the sociopaths act out their conflicts with authority and for this reason further encourage the disruptive behavior. The consultant should help administrators and staff recognize the problem, set firm limits, and, when necessary, evict the antisocial patient.

Another problem that frequently arises when consulting to residential facilities is that of helping the administrator and staff understand and deal with the *symbiotic relationship*. Many referring professionals use out-of-home placements in an attempt to help patients extricate themselves from symbiotic family ties. Although the therapist may think it beneficial that such relationships be broken, or at least weakened, patients and their families may not agree, even though they may pay lip service to the idea. Such relationships, like many neurotic marriages, often seem quite pathological to outside observers. They may be right, but the relationship may meet many needs and the participants may be unwilling or unable, even with our help, to give it up. A patient will frequently go along with a plan for separation in order to please the therapist. Perhaps the main point to be emphasized here is that the decision to separate is ultimately up to the patient and the family. Except under extreme conditions, the therapist's role should be that of clarifying options and certainly not exerting pressure. It has been shown, moreover, that even where the interpersonal relationships are difficult, families can be helped to become a supportive primary resource for the schizophrenic patient (Goldstein and Kopeikin, 1981). The residential care staffs should realize that a patient's desire to return home, or the family's pressing for a return, may simply be a function of family dynamics and not reflect on the quality of care at the facility.

A Final Word

A large proportion of chronically mentally ill persons live in community residential facilities run by administrators and staff who are not specifically trained in the management of psychiatric patients; this situation makes consultation to residential facilities an issue of high priority. Consultants should be familiar with the facility's operating procedures, with the wide range of social and vocational potential among long-term patients, and with the needs of certain patients for highly structured programs. They should be aware of the facility administrator's attitude toward mental health professionals and be prepared to deal with problems that can arise when they attempt to provide both consultation and direct service to the same facility. Consultants should advise administrators on such issues as determining admission criteria, dealing with the schizophrenic patient's difficulty in tolerating intimacy, establishing house government, handling the problem of alcohol and drugs, managing antisocial personality disorders, and understanding and dealing with symbiotic family relationships.

❧ Six ❧

The Therapeutic Use of Structure

That some patients might need to reside in a long-term, locked, intensively supervised community facility was a foreign thought to many who advocated return to the community in the early years of emptying the state hospitals. "Patients who need a secure environment can remain in the state hospital" was the rationale. But in those early years most people seemed to think that such patients were few and that community treatment and modern psychoactive medications would take care of most problems. More people are now recognizing that a number of severely disabled patients present major problems in management and can survive outside of state hospitals only if they have a sufficiently structured facility in the community (Lamb, 1976). What are the characteristics of such patients and what kinds of problems do they present? The purpose of this chapter is to answer these questions and then to describe a highly structured community facility that, in my opinion, exemplifies a treatment setting ideally suited to these patients. Although this chapter is largely concerned with a particular type of facility, it should be emphasized that structure does not necessarily mean a locked door (see Chapter Four).

Note: This chapter is a revised and expanded version of a paper by the author entitled "Structure: The Neglected Ingredient of Community Treatment," *Archives of General Psychiatry*, 1980, *37* (11), 1224–1228.

Why not simply leave these patients in the state hospital? This question is often expressed as an exhortation in this age of polarization of views between those advocating hospital treatment and those advocating community treatment (Bennett, 1978). Another purpose of this chapter, then, is to explore the advantages of a community alternative to the state hospital for this group of patients. This community alternative helps to explain why California, with its population of 23,668,562 (1980 Census), had less than 3,000 psychiatric patients in state hospitals in 1982.

The needs of long-term, severely disabled patients living in the community vary greatly (Scherl and Macht, 1979). However, no need is more important or varies more widely than the degree of structure these patients require in their living situations. Some need a minimum of structure and can handle independent living. Others can manage an approximation of independent living with some support and structure, such as a satellite housing program where an agency provides ongoing support with regular group meetings, crisis intervention, and home visits. Since the agency usually holds the lease, patients are also relieved of a responsibility and commitment, which many long-term, severely disabled patients are unable to handle.

A large proportion of long-term, severely disabled patients in the community require moderate amounts of support and structure; perhaps a third of the long-term patients in California live in board-and-care homes (described in Chapter Four). In these open settings, patients are provided structure in the form of room and board, varying degrees of supervision, some treatment (especially psychoactive medications; often each dose is dispensed to them), and brief visits with a psychiatrist. These functions are not unlike those of the old, custodial state hospital. Thus, for a large proportion of the long-term psychiatric patients, the board-and-care home, or in some states the intermediate care facility (ICF), has not only replaced the state hospital as a place to live but has taken over many of the functions of the state hospital as well (Lamb, 1979b). Probably about half of the long-term, severely disabled patients in the community live with relatives (Lamb and Goertzel, 1977), where they receive varying degrees of support and structure.

A number of long-term, severely disabled psychiatric patients lack sufficient impulse control to handle living in an open setting such as a board-and-care home or with relatives (see Chapter Four). They need a high degree of external structure and control to compensate for the inadequacy of their own internal controls. The total number of such patients may not be great when compared with the total population of severely disabled patients. If placed in community living arrangements without sufficient structure, however, this group can easily be disruptive to the community and take up a large proportion of the time of mental health professionals, not to mention other agencies such as the police. More important, they may be impulsively self-destructive or present a physical danger to others. This group of patients is the focus of this chapter.

Now let us turn to a study of eighty patients living in a locked, skilled-nursing facility for psychiatric patients only, with a special treatment program for the mentally disabled. The primary method of study was a series of in-depth psychiatric interviews I conducted with each patient.

Setting

The facility chosen for this study was a ninety-five-bed, locked, skilled-nursing facility devoted solely to treatment and rehabilitation of the mentally ill. There are currently thirty-one such facilities in California. To explore the potential of the concept as fully as possible, I selected a facility that was generally held in high regard by mental health professionals in the area. This facility, now fourteen years old, is located on a major street of a small city twenty-five miles east of downtown Los Angeles. Its physical appearance is pleasant, even attractive. It has been converted from a facility for the physically ill (nursing home) to its present use primarily by locking the door, bolting the windows shut, and substituting transparent plastic windows for regular glass windows. In the somewhat euphemistic words of the program brochure: "This facility specializes in the rehabilitation of the chronic psychiatric patient who is in need of a highly structured environment. For this reason our exterior doors and windows are locked as a reminder to the patient that he is under treatment. This also assures the family that the patient will be supervised without fear of outside distraction."

There is close supervision of medication: approximately three fifths of the patients receive their medication in either liquid or crushed form. The staff/patient ratio is high. There is a full-time nursing staff of twenty-one, of whom nine are licensed (registered nurses or licensed practical nurses). There are, in addition, thirteen full-time "program staff" members who have bachelor's degrees or experience as psychiatric aides and some college courses. Two adult-education teachers, paid by the local school district, spend half to three fourths of their time in the facility. This staff provides an activity program of at least twenty-seven hours weekly for each patient. Included are various group therapies, instruction in the activities of daily living, and a full range of social and recreational therapeutic activities. The teachers give classes in basic education and also help patients prepare to take their high school equivalency exams. Emphasis is placed on limiting illegal drugs, alcohol, and sexual freedom. Passes into the neighboring community with other patients, and often with staff, and passes home are possible for many when they have demonstrated their ability to handle varying amounts of freedom.

With the exception of a few patients who pay privately, the full cost for this facility is billed to Medicaid, which pays the skilled-nursing facility rate (fiscal year 1980–1981) of $39 a day plus a $5 a day differential for the psychiatric treatment and rehabilitation program. Thus the total cost is $44 per day, which includes everything except the medication interviews with the visiting psychiatrist; the psychiatrists bill separately to Medicaid.

Method

All eighty-nine patients currently living in the facility were approached; nine refused to participate, leaving a sample of eighty persons. I then conducted an in-depth interview with each patient. Although an interview guide covered demographic data, pertinent history, and all aspects of their current lives, I tried to encourage an informal, comfortable and wide-ranging conversation and also chatted with residents in the halls. Moreover, I consulted the medical records kept in the facility: discharge summaries from referring professionals and institutions as well as progress notes by the two private psychiatrists who visit the facility for medication management. I obtained additional information from the facility's staff.

Results

Demographic Characteristics and Diagnoses. This was primarily a young population; the median age was twenty-five, with a range of eighteen to sixty-three years. The population was almost equally divided between men ($N = 41$) and women ($N = 39$). The median age, twenty-five years, was the same for both men (range: eighteen to sixty-two years) and women (range: eighteen to sixty-three years). Sixty-six of the patients were Caucasian, six were black, four were Hispanic, and four were Oriental. More than three fourths (sixty-three) had never been married; three were married, twelve were divorced or separated, and two were widowed. The patients' median education was eleventh grade, with a range from seventh grade to two years of graduate school.

Of the eighty patients, seventy-eight (98 percent) had diagnoses of psychoses (schizophrenic disorders for sixty-three and affective disorders for fifteen), one had a diagnosis of personality disorder, and one had a diagnosis of organic brain syndrome. As for source of support, seventy (88 percent) received Supplemental Security Income, eight had no funds, one received Social Security Disability payments, and one received a Veterans Administration pension.

The median length of stay at this facility was twelve months, with a range of two weeks to seventy-eight months. Some 51 percent (forty-one) were voluntary patients and 49 percent (thirty-nine) were under conservatorship. Conservatorship is a legal status established by the California Lanterman-Petris-Short Act; a court may declare persons who are gravely disabled (as a result of mental disorder unable to provide for their basic personal needs for food, clothing, and shelter) to be wards of a public agency such as the public guardian or wards of a private conservator (generally a relative) for one-year renewable periods. The conservator has the power to place the patient involuntarily in a hospital or facility such as this one for an indefinite period and to manage the patient's money. Further, the conservator can compel the patient to live in an open facility such as a board-and-care home.

Some pertinent findings by sex are given in Table 1. Fifty-eight percent had a history of violence either in the community, in mental health facilities, or in both. This figure includes violence against persons and property. The percentage for men (66 percent) is greater than that for women (49 percent), but the difference is not statistically significant. Forty-one percent had physically assaulted persons within the previous twelve months (21 percent men and 20 percent women).

Psychopathology. To assess psychopathology, the five-point psychiatric assessment scales developed by Krawiecka, Goldberg, and Vaughan (1977) were used. The presence of severe, overt psychopathology was defined as the manifestation of major or severe symptoms in at least two of the following three scales: delusions, hallucinations, and thought disorder (incoherence and irrelevance of speech). Using this definition, 60 percent of the sample exhibited severe, overt psychopathology.

Sixty percent of the study population had been hospitalized at least once in a state hospital in their lifetime. Seventy-three percent had proved unmanageable in at least one previous placement in a board-and-care home or other out-of-home placement. Thirty-nine percent had at some point in their lives held a job for six months or longer.

Patients were considered to have goals if they expressed a desire to change anything in their lives, such as social or vocational activity or living situation after discharge, whether or not the achievement of these goals seemed realistic. Only psychotic goals ("to live forever") were not counted. Using this definition, 81 percent had goals.

Behavior. Efforts were made to determine what kinds of problem behavior preceded, and probably contributed to, patients being placed in this highly structured community facility. In 73 percent (fifty-eight) of the cases, less structured open settings had failed to control and stabilize these patients. Among these less structured settings were board-and-care homes, halfway houses, and open skilled-nursing facilities. In almost all of the other cases, placement in open settings had not been attempted because in the judgment of the

Table 1. Findings on Eighty Patients in a Locked Skilled-Nursing Mental Health Facility.

| | N (%) | | | | | |
| | Male | | Female | | Total | |
Characteristic	Yes	No	Yes	No	Yes	No
History of violence	27 (66)	14 (34)	19 (49)	20 (51)	46 (58)	34 (43)
Major psychopathology	23 (56)	18 (44)	25 (64)	14 (36)	48 (60)	32 (40)
At least one state hospitalization	26 (63)	15 (37)	22 (56)	17 (44)	48 (60)	32 (40)
Unmanageable in one or more board-and-care homes or other open facility	31 (76)	10 (24)	27 (69)	12 (31)	58 (73)	22 (28)
Held job more than 6 months	16 (39)	25 (61)	15 (38)	24 (62)	31 (39)	49 (61)
Goals	33 (80)	8 (20)	32 (82)	7 (18)	65 (81)	15 (19)

Note: None of the male-female differences are statistically significant.

referring professionals there was extreme out-of-control behavior or serious self-destructive behavior. The exceptions were two patients who were already in the facility when it was converted five years previously into a locked mental health facility; the staff had become fond of these patients and felt protective toward them.

Because of the difficulty of predicting dangerousness, this study sought only to determine if patients had been physically assaultive to others within the previous twelve months. Forty-one percent (thirty-three) had been so. Eleven percent of the patients (nine) were judged by both the staff and the investigator to be too frightening to others to be tolerated in an open setting where others are uncertain whether these patients can and will be controlled. Eight percent (six patients) were judged by the facility staff and this investigator to be dangerous to themselves. Four of them had made previous suicide attempts and were judged by both the facility staff and the investigator still to be dangerous to themselves. The reliability of our judgments of being frightening to others and dangerous to themselves is open to question, of course, since they are clinical opinions and not demonstrable facts.

Two female schizophrenic patients, aged nineteen and twenty years, had a history of repeatedly running away, living on the streets, and becoming involved in drugs and prostitution. Since neither was considered "streetwise" or able to survive on the streets, they were placed in this facility to protect them from what mental health professionals and their families considered a self-destructive course.

Thirty-five percent of the patients (twenty-eight) had a diagnosis of psychosis and also a severe drug or alcohol problem (or both). Eight percent of the patients (six) showed a pattern of repeatedly becoming psychotic and being rehospitalized when living with their family, but at the same time neither patient nor family seemed able to remain separated when the patient was placed in an open out-of-home setting. Eighty-one percent (sixty-five) of the patients resisted taking psychoactive medications or had a history of noncompliance with medication regimens in open settings.

Comment

This was essentially a young population (median age: twenty-five years). Furthermore, 41 percent had physically assaulted others within the previous twelve months. These figures should be considered in conjunction with those of a previous study of persons sent to a state hospital from a county where an attempt is made to treat as many patients as possible in local inpatient facilities (Lamb, 1977). In that earlier study, issues of violence and control were involved in 60 percent of the sample of patients sent to the state hospital—and among the males in that study, whose median age was 24.5 years, 71 percent of the cases were characterized by issues of violence and control. Thus similarities emerge between the patients at the locked, skilled-nursing facility assessed in this study and the core group of patients sent to the state hospital in the earlier study in terms of the kinds of patients considered appropriate for both.

The percentage of patients exhibiting severe, overt psychopathology (60 percent) is high—especially when compared with a third study, already described in Chapter Four (Lamb, 1979b), of all the residents of a board-and-care home in Los Angeles, where 32 percent exhibited severe, overt psychopathology using the same criteria as in the present study. Patients in the present study were considered unmanageable in board-and-care homes and other open settings; these settings had already failed with three fourths of these persons, and the behavior of all but two of the others had caused professionals to judge that they too could not be managed there. Over four fifths of those in the present study are currently resistant to taking psychotropic medications or have a history of noncompliance with medication regimens in open settings. Over a third of the patients have both a diagnosis of psychosis and a severe alcohol or drug problem (or both); this group of mentally ill patients who also abuse drugs and alcohol is one of the most difficult to manage, let alone treat, in community settings.

Thus we find in this facility an extremely difficult group of patients in terms of management in community settings. Their problems are not unlike those found in the residual group of patients left behind in state hospitals after deinstitutionalization (Dorwart, 1980). The patients in this study are characterized by assaultive behavior; severe, overt major psychopathology; lack of internal controls; reluctance to take psychotropic medications; inability to adjust to open settings; problems with drugs and alcohol; and, in some cases, self-destructive behavior. Moreover, some are frightening to others because of their appearance and/or actions.

It should be noted that approximately half these patients were voluntary and half involuntary (placed in this facility by their conservator). Conservatorship thus provides structure in the lives of these patients. This structure can continue after discharge when the conservator can compel the patient to live in an open facility such as a board-and-care home and perhaps interrupt a chaotic life-style on the streets—a life-style characterized by repeated crises, hospitalization, and time in jail.

Advantages of the Locked Skilled-Nursing Facility. This locked, skilled-nursing facility, then, fulfills the function of the state hospital for patients who would be among its more difficult charges. This point is especially important, for when one attempts to manage these patients in less structured community settings (as is frequently the case in community mental health programs), they tend to take up an inordinate share of the time and effort of mental health professionals. Furthermore, some of these patients might otherwise be in hospitals for the criminally insane—as, for instance, the two who have been sex offenders and some who have been involved in criminal activities such as passing bad checks, forgery, robbery, and auto theft.

Bachrach (1978) notes that deinstitutionalization efforts have, in practice, too often confused locus of care and quality of care. (That is, care in the community has been assumed almost by definition to be good.) She stresses the importance of studying the patient's level of functioning, attempting to place the patient in the setting most compatible with that level, and then carrying the process one step further by helping develop the patient's skills. The locked skilled-nursing facility in this study, with its special programs for the mentally ill, gives patients in need of structure a chance at treatment and rehabilitation in a setting in their home community. The intensive program that schedules most of the patient's day is another key element in providing structure. This approach is in contrast to simply putting patients in an isolated, large state hospital where the treatment may be inadequate or impersonal and foster a life of institutional regression. Thus, these patients have an opportunity to make progress before being placed in a long-term custodial setting.

Still another advantage is its size of less than a hundred beds. (Some similar facilities are still smaller, ranging from 30 to 150 beds.) Since this smaller size (as compared with a state hospital) makes it possible for every staff member in the facility to know every patient, it contributes to making the treatment milieu more personal. Furthermore, with the high ratio of staff to patients it is possible to develop an individualized treatment and rehabilitation program for each patient and to give patients the feeling that they are in fact individuals who are being treated as such. Recall that this facility has a reputation of being a particularly good one and that for these benefits to be realized, there must be dedicated and competent administration and staff.

We need to learn from the history of state hospitals in the United States and keep the size of these facilities small—no more than a hundred beds. The state hospitals began as small, well-run, therapeutic facilities and gradually were expanded to the huge institutions we know today. We must therefore resist adding on a wing here and a wing there and keep these facilities small, by statute if need be. Likewise, staffing patterns must be maintained at levels conducive to individualized therapy, and sufficient treatment and rehabilitation programs must be mandated.

Patient Characteristics and Treatment Milieu. The milieu emphasizes not simply structure but also goals; each patient is encouraged to make effective use of the program even though it may take several years. It was found that 81 percent of the patients at this facility professed to have goals. This number is consistent with the findings of long-term patients living in a board-and-care home (Lamb, 1979b), where it was found that 68 percent of the younger patients (under age thirty) had goals as opposed to only 43 percent of the older patients (over age thirty). This study group had a median age of twenty-five years. The fact that four fifths of these patients have goals may be related to the philosophy and culture of the facility, but it also seems likely that it is related at least in part to the youthfulness of the patients. It is especially important to work intensively with these young patients while they still have goals, have had less time to settle into a life of regression, and, one hopes, are still motivated to make changes in their lives.

Periodic staff reviews look closely at this issue of goals, and patients who refuse to involve themselves in the program are considered for transfer to a less treatment-oriented facility. One of the primary goals of the program is not only to involve patients in active treatment but to prepare them for living in a less structured setting. Thus there is an attempt to limit the length of stay to the least time necessary to achieve this goal of needing less structure. The emphasis on reducing the length of stay at the locked skilled-nursing facility can be a motivating factor for the patient to make progress and not simply become institutionalized in this setting.

Structure and the Family. These patients no longer require a short-term treatment hospital, but they have exceeded the ability of their families to manage them at home and tolerate their behavior. With the patient in a structured community setting, however, most (86 percent) are seen regularly by their families and 38 percent have passes at home, 30 percent have overnight passes, and 8 percent have passes for the day only. If a weekend pass goes badly, a conference can be held with the patient and family to resolve the problem. If the patient or family is not ready for passes, the passes can be terminated by the family—or by the facility if the family is too guilt-ridden or otherwise unable to set this kind of limit. This policy takes pressure off the family and at the same time sets the needed limits on the patient.

Sometimes the patient and family feel ambivalent about one another. The family may not want or cannot tolerate or may be afraid to have the patient at home, at least on a full-time basis. If patients want to go home or believe they are needed there, however, the family may feel a need to encourage this desire or give the patient a mixed message about coming home because of ambivalence or guilt. Only a locked setting, then, can contain the patient and prevent an impulsive return home to what quickly becomes a chaotic situation resulting in rehospitalization.

A Final Word

Many workers in community mental health deny their patients' need for structure; too often they fail to note the degree of structure required when assessing patients' needs in community placement. And since structure is not provided in the community, these persons are condemned to repeated decompensations and re-hospitalizations (the revolving door syndrome) or long periods in state hospitals. At the same time, many professionals working in hospitals, both state and local, take the hospital structure, and the patient's resulting sense of security, for granted. Thus, they too do not take into account in their community planning the fact that most community settings do not have this degree of structure. Failing to recognize the patients who need structure, they send them out to insufficiently structured placements and thus contribute to patients' repeated decompensation and rehospitalization.

❧ Seven ❧

Young Adult
Chronic Patients:
The New Drifters

In the universal search for meaning in life, many long-term severely disabled psychiatric patients find only emptiness. A positive sense of meaning in life is usually associated with membership in groups, dedication to some cause, and adoption of clear life goals (Yalom, 1980). In all these areas, long-term patients generally fall short.

My study of long-term severely disabled psychiatric patients in a board-and-care home in Los Angeles showed that significantly more patients under age thirty than over age thirty desired to change something in their lives (Lamb, 1979b). What does this finding mean? Perhaps, as these persons with limited capabilities become older, they experience repeated failures in dealing with life's demands and achieving their earlier goals. They have had more time to lower or set aside their goals and accept a low level of functioning that does not exceed their capabilities. In the same study, a strong relationship was found between age and history of hospitalization; three fourths of those under age thirty had been hospitalized during the preceding year, compared with only one fifth over age thirty.

Note: This chapter is a revised and expanded version of a paper by the author in *Hospital & Community Psychiatry*, 1982, *33* (6).

Young people who are just beginning to deal with life's demands and make their way in the world are struggling to achieve a measure of independence, to choose and succeed at a vocation, to establish satisfying interpersonal relationships and attain some degree of intimacy, and to acquire a sense of identity. Because the mentally ill lack ego strength, the capacity to withstand stress, and the ability to form meaningful interpersonal relationships, their efforts often lead only to failure. The result may be a still more determined, even frantic, effort with a greatly increased level of anxiety that begins to border on desperation. Ultimately the anxiety may lead to yet another failure accompanied by feelings of despair. For a person predisposed to retreat into psychosis, repeated failures lead to a stormy course with acute psychotic breaks and hospitalizations. The situation becomes compounded when such persons are in an environment where unrealistic expectations emanate not just from within themselves but also from families and mental health professionals.

Some chronically dysfunctional and mentally disordered individuals gradually, over a period of years, succeed in their strivings for independence, a vocation, intimacy, and a sense of identity. Many others, however, eventually give up the struggle and find face-saving rationalizations for their limited degree of functioning and accomplishments. A middle-aged woman says, "I would have raised my children, but the judge was lied to and took them away from me." Or someone in his middle years says, "I am retired now on Social Security," when in fact he receives Supplemental Security Income because of his disabling psychiatric disorder. Similar rationalizations come from chronically dysfunctional persons who feel they must passively submit to overwhelming forces that control their destinies and impede their progress. Often one eventually hears no rationalizations at all but finds only a constricted passive stance on life. An example would be the patients who seem to look no further than their next cigarette.

Thus, as patients age, much of the pressure that used to result in psychotic decompensations is removed. Maturation also plays its part, since age makes people less impulsive and "more philosophical" in the face of adversity and disappointment.

Facing the Crisis of Age Thirty

Chronically disabled patients, both young and old, are disheartened and depressed, just as we all would be, about not having goals, about not being able to reach goals, about experiencing repeated failures instead. Concerns about getting older with little to show for one's life are felt not only by those in the involutional period but also by those who are approaching age thirty and even by those still in their mid-twenties.

As one approaches and then reaches thirty, there is inevitably a process of assessing one's achievements, or lack of them, and judging the extent to which goals set for this age have been reached. Nearing age thirty seems to be a time of settling down, a time for taking life more seriously and giving up the "frivolities" of youth, a time to marry or establish a permanent relationship, to be at least launched on a career, to consolidate one's plans. When the assessment of one's life at this age is not positive, many feel that life has not been worthwhile and are beset by feelings of inadequacy and depression. This point may seem self-evident, yet all too often we tend to forget that long-term, severely mentally ill patients are affected by the stresses and concerns of each phase of the life cycle and have the same existential concerns as we all do.

Before deinstitutionalization these patients, who have been called the new chronic patients, were chronically institutionalized, often at the time of their first psychotic break in adolescence or early adulthood. Sometimes they improved in the hospital and were discharged but at their next decompensation were rehospitalized, never to return to the community. Thus, after their initial failures in trying to cope with the vicissitudes of life and of living in the community, they were no longer exposed to these stresses: They were given permanent asylum from the demands of the world.

Now hospital stays tend to be brief. In this sense, most of the new long-term patients are the products of deinstitutionalization. This is not to imply that we should turn the clock back and return to a system of total institutionalization for all long-term patients. In the community these patients can have something very precious— their liberty, to the extent they can handle it. Further, if we provide the resources, they can realize their potential for successfully passing some of life's milestones.

Only three decades ago there were no psychoactive medications to bring such patients out of their world of autistic fantasy and put reality into clearer perspective. It was also more difficult to return them to the community. Even today many patients fail to take their psychoactive medications in order to avoid the dysphoric feelings of depression and anxiety that result when they see their reality too clearly; they prefer a blurring of reality to a relative normality induced by medication (Van Putten, Crumpton, and Yale, 1976). Psychoactive medications help prevent long-term hospitalization, which previously kept long-term patients from trying to find a place for themselves in the world. But, at the same time, medications have denied to these patients the simple gratification offered by long-term asylum from stress.

The new chronic patients are often reluctant to see themselves as different from anyone else and thus tend to deny a need for mental health treatment (Pepper, Kirshner, and Ryglewicz, 1981). In their eyes, to admit mental illness is to admit failure. Many feel that becoming part of the mental health system is like joining an army of misfits (Estroff, 1981). Moreover, mental health professionals to whom these patients are brought for help are often not accepted as helpers but rather become convenient targets (as are their parents and society generally) onto whom they can displace the "blame" for their situation and their failures. Instead of accepting treatment, many medicate themselves with street drugs; thus they gain admittance to the drug subculture, where they can find acceptance despite their lack of status in the conventional sense.

Another factor contributing to these patients' refusal of treatment is the natural rebelliousness of youth, a normal part of the process of striving for autonomy; one feels a sense of independence when taking a position contrary to parents or society (or, in this instance, contrary to the mental health establishment). In the normal course of events, persons who feel secure in their independence can begin to moderate their positions without feeling they have lost their newfound liberty. With most long-term patients, it is a lack of readiness for independence—a lack they may or may not be able to acknowledge and of which they may not even be aware—that sooner or later necessitates their accepting patienthood.

If we do not keep these dynamics in mind, and even if we do, we may find a sizable number of young chronic patients provocative, aggravating, and infuriating, however great our tolerance and resourcefulness (Schwartz and Goldfinger, 1981). They alternately demand and reject care, and we find ourselves confronted in turn or all at once with dependency, manipulation, withdrawal, anger, depression, and at times what amounts to psychological extortion. It should be emphasized that such patients constitute only one subgroup of young chronic patients; they do not represent the total population (Sheets, Prevost, and Reihman, 1982). Their low tolerance of frustration and lack of impulse control frequently result in encounters with the law. They do not make good use of mental health services, do not take their prescribed medications, and generally do not follow reasonable treatment plans. And since they have alienated family, friends, and the rest of their community support system, the full burden of their care at times of crisis falls upon the mental health service system. The result is severe system stress (Bachrach, 1982). Moreover, a frequent response of mental health professionals to this subgroup of young chronic patients is to find a way to terminate their treatment relationships with them prematurely (Schwartz and Goldfinger, 1981).

Another subgroup of young chronic patients identified by Sheets and his coworkers (1982) are passive, poorly motivated, and accepting of mental health services to the point of marked dependence upon the mental health system. They function poorly even in remission and appear burned out at an early age. Still a third group functions well in remission, though there may be considerable disability beneath their facade of apparent competence. They are often isolated individuals with limited social supports. Their reluctance to engage in traditional mental health programs stems not from adolescent rebellion but from a desire to blend into the general population without being identified as mental patients. They do, however, crave mastery over their condition and want to know how to prevent relapses. As with any categorization, of course, there is considerable overlap between the three groups.

Issues of Control and Violence

A critical problem in working with some young psychotic patients is dealing with matters of control and violence. For a small but important group of young patients, there are difficult problems of control and management in community settings. Many of these patients are characterized by assaultive behavior, severe overt psychopathology, lack of internal controls, reluctance to take psychotropic medications, an inability to adjust to open settings, problems with drugs and alcohol in addition to their psychoses, and, in some cases, self-destructive behavior. They often require highly structured community settings such as locked skilled-nursing facilities or extended stays in state hospitals. (See Chapter Six.)

Assessing the need for external control and structure is essential. When an attempt is made to manage patients in less structured community settings, as in community mental health programs, these patients, though relatively few in number, tend to take up an inordinate share of the time and effort of mental health professionals. Further, although acting out defiantly, rebelliously, and violently may be an attempt to achieve independence and individuation, the community may not be able to tolerate the actions of patients who do not demonstrate sufficient self-control. Often overlooked by professionals are the effects of violent acts on the patients who have committed them, especially if the victim is a close relative, friend, or caretaker. The aftermath may be a web of guilt and remorse that only compounds the patient's problems. Further, the realization of having once lost control and the fear of losing it again can be extremely anxiety-producing.

The New Drifters

Drifter is a word that strikes a chord in all those who have contact with young, chronic patients—mental health professionals, families, and the patients themselves. Some drifters wander from community to community seeking a geographic solution to their problems; hoping to leave their problems behind, they find they have simply brought them to a new location. Others drift in the community from one living situation to another. Still others, though they remain in one place, can best be described as drifting through life: They lead lives without goals, direction, or ties other than perhaps a hostile-dependent relationship with parents or other caretakers.

Why do they drift? Apart from their desire to outrun their problems, their symptoms, and their failures, they have great difficulty achieving closeness and intimacy. A fantasy of finding closeness elsewhere encourages them to move on. Yet all too often, if they do stumble into an intimate relationship or find themselves in a residence where there is caring and closeness and sharing, the increased anxiety they experience creates a need to run.

They drift also in search of autonomy, as a way of denying their dependency and out of a desire for an isolated life-style. And they drift because of a reluctance to become involved in a mental health treatment program or a supportive out-of-home environment, such as a halfway house or board-and-care home, that would give them a mental patient identity and make them part of the mental health system; they do not want to see themselves as ill.

As we saw in Chapter Four, those who move from one board-and-care home to another tend to be young; they may be trying to escape the pull of dependency and may not be ready to come to terms with living in a sheltered, segregated, low-pressure environment. Those who move on are still apt to have life goals but are also apt to have been hospitalized during the preceding year (Lamb, 1980a). Some may regard leaving their comparatively static milieu as a necessary part of the process of realizing their goals—but a process that exacts its price in terms of crisis, decompensation, and hospitalizations.

Approaching the Problems

What can be done to begin to resolve the problems of the new, young, long-term patient? Establishing an array of high-quality community treatment and rehabilitation resources is clearly a crucial first step. We now know enough about the kinds of resources that are most effective for many of these patients (Pepper and Ryglewicz, 1982) and mental health decision makers are beginning to see that these patients should receive our highest priority. But in the

meantime we must not be carried away by the concepts of mainstreaming and normalization when these goals are unrealistic. We
must recognize that we can contribute a great deal to the lives of
long-term patients whether or not they are capable, socially and
vocationally, of becoming fully functioning members of society.
Improving the quality of life for these patients is itself an important
objective.

What about the young chronic patients for whom life seems
to hold no meaning? Engagement is the therapeutic answer to meaninglessness. To quote Yalom (1980, p. 482): "To find a home, to
care about other individuals, about ideas or projects, to search, to
create, to build—these, and all other forms of engagement, are twice
rewarding: they are intrinsically enriching, and they alleviate the
dysphoria that stems from being bombarded with the unassembled
brute data of existence." Engagement is the answer, too, for the new
drifters, though the extent to which they can become engaged varies
greatly.

It is especially important to work intensively with young
patients while they still have goals, have had less time to settle into a
life of regression, and, one hopes, are still motivated to make
changes in their lives. We must be sure that their goals, and ours, are
realistic. If the limits of a patient's capabilities are a sheltered workshop or at best an entry-level job, we should support this endeavor.
Such an activity might seem demeaning to us, or might seem inappropriate for an intelligent patient from an achieving family, but it
might well give patients a feeling of productivity and self-respect
they have never known before. We must be sure that the pace is one
patients can handle. We must not let their impatience, or ours,
propel them onto a fast track to failure. And we must provide, or
help them find, sufficient support during this difficult period.

A Final Word

We have discussed these young people's quest for autonomy,
their fear of being labeled as psychiatric misfits, and the reluctance
of many to accept our services. In many cases we can persuade these
young persons to enter our programs; but in many others we cannot (Bachrach, 1982). Unless patients' behavior becomes so self-

destructive that their safety and well-being are compromised, or their behavior becomes more destructive or disruptive than society can tolerate, we must often learn to wait until maturity has shifted the balance or the patient has found a way to rationalize turning to us. If we have an opportunity to see patients over long periods of time, we may find that we must wait for years, through repeated crises and many attempts to involve them with us, before we finally succeed in engaging them in treatment and rehabilitation.

It is important that we try to minimize our disappointment if our offers of help are rejected; we need to accept that our powers of persuasion are limited. Otherwise our feelings of disappointment are communicated to patients, who experience them as a sign that once again they have failed to measure up. We also need to focus on the problems and concerns of turning thirty. Thus we should offer programs, within the patients' capabilities, to help them acquire a vocational identity. We should respond to their assessment of themselves as people who cannot cope by offering supports—living arrangements geared to their needs, psychoactive medications, a stable source of income. In these ways we can help to stabilize our patients' lives in the community and demonstrate to them that it is within their power, by accepting these supports, to eliminate the chaos in their lives. At the same time the patient needs to see that everyone, not just psychiatric patients, needs a support system to cope with life's demands.

Helping patients develop rationalizations will sometimes facilitate their adjustment. For instance, one can help them delay entry into situations beyond their capabilities, such as a demanding vocational program or a more independent living situation, by encouraging them to see the delay as part of their convalescence from a "nervous breakdown" or from years "out in the cold." Such a delay may or may not be temporary. Even if it turns out to be permanent, it has been a face-saving way for patients to avoid a situation they cannot handle. They have been spared a psychotic episode or the need to run, or drift, from their treatment. Later the problem can be dealt with in a more definitive way.

Who among us faces all the realities of our lives without the use of rationalization? If we examine the therapy of healthier patients than these, we usually consider ourselves successful if patients come to terms with the realities of their lives. And that usually means they rationalize to some degree—not simply that they face squarely all the stark realities of their past, present, and future.

Finally, we should not forget the importance of the one-to-one relationship between trained helping professionals and their patients. This is an age in which the treatment of long-term patients often consists of psychoactive medications accompanied only by "coordination" by relatively untrained persons of services that may not exist or may be impossible to coordinate. We should keep in mind the capabilities, or lack of them, of our patients, their reactions to the stresses of the life cycle, and their failures to meet society's expectations and their own. And we should provide professionals trained to listen, trained to assess patients' capabilities, trained to reinforce patients' rationalizations when it is appropriate, trained to encourage productivity when it is possible, and trained to help patients find their own level of independence, engagement, and personal dignity.

❧ Eight ❧

Families of the Mentally Ill

There have been important developments in recent years in regard to families of the mentally ill. First of all, families have organized, developed a new self-concept, and become a force to be reckoned with. Moreover, many professionals have come to see families from a new perspective and there has evolved an approach to help them that is both sensitive and practical. These developments are the subject of this chapter.

In the past, the parents of schizophrenics have generally accepted passively whatever treatment was meted out to them. Increasingly, however, they are finding this passive stance unacceptable. In fact, the organization of patients' relatives as advocacy and mutual support groups has become a significant phenomenon. But this significance has gone virtually unrecognized by many mental health professionals who do not realize that they will be increasingly affected and held accountable by these relatives' groups. As these associations become more powerful and politically sophisticated, we will be reminded more and more forcefully when we have been insensitive to the needs of the severely mentally ill and their families.

Note: Parts of this chapter appeared in a chapter by the author and Eve Oliphant entitled "Parents of Schizophrenics: Advocates for the Mentally Ill," *New Directions for Mental Health Services: Community Support Systems for the Long-Term Patient,* no. 2 (San Francisco: Jossey-Bass, 1979).

Moreover, relatives have become the real "primary care" agents for a large proportion of schizophrenics in this era of deinstitutionalization (Creer and Wing, 1974). But this seemingly obvious fact has also gone almost unnoticed by many mental health professionals—despite the numbers of patients involved. In a recent study of long-term severely disabled patients in the community, for instance, more than 50 percent were living with relatives (Lamb and Goertzel, 1977). Only recently, however, has attention begun to be turned to the problems of dealing with chronic schizophrenic patients at home. Relatives must learn to live with and deal with unpredictable behavior, never knowing how the patient will react to a situation at a particular time, even to the point of occasional violence. The patient's lack of conversation is an acute problem for a relative such as the spouse who depends on the patient for companionship. Relatives must come to terms with the patient's social withdrawal, underactivity, excessive sleeping, and socially embarrassing behavior. If the patient and relative stay together, in time they may reach an equilibrium that enables the patient to live outside a hospital but at the expense of restricting the lives of the family. Often the relative cannot leave the house even to go shopping without getting someone to watch the patient. The relatives may not only become like jailers but, in effect, be in jail themselves.

Further, Arieti (1974) has observed that schizophrenics tend to attribute to their parents full responsibility for their illness and despair, absolving themselves from guilt and closing off examination of their own part in the development of illness. Unfortunately, many mental health professionals have accepted these perceptions of the family in toto as accurate accounts of historical events. Arieti believes that generally the patient's view is highly distorted and exaggerated; it is the therapist's job to help patients get their parents into perspective and stop blaming others for all their troubles. Patients need to recognize the role of others in their lives, but they also need to assume some responsibility for what happened to them in the past and especially for their current and future actions (Arieti, 1975). For a detailed discussion of these issues, see Chapter Ten.

Far from recognizing these problems and these insights, many professionals lay all the blame for the patients' problems at the parents' doorstep. Many schools of psychiatric thought implicate the patients' families in aggravating and even generating their illness (Appleton, 1974). Moreover, they forget that being the relative of a mentally ill person is already traumatic and often overwhelming. Usually the family, even before its contact with the mental health establishment, is guilt-ridden and feels a keen sense of failure for having "produced" a schizophrenic. Professionals are often insufficiently aware of this feeling and of the additional impact of a parent's receiving a label like "schizophrenogenic mother." The concept of the "identified patient"—the idea that the entire family is ill and the patient is simply the person who has been labeled as the sick one—adds further trauma; to the parents it means not only that they have driven their child crazy but that the whole family is sick as well.

Moreover, long-term schizophrenics have frequently been given low priority in community mental health programs (Hogarty, 1971; Kirk and Therrien, 1975). Community mental health has often focused on prevention and on those who have problems in living— people who have not been hospitalized and will never need to be. California is one of the states in which a number of state hospitals have been closed, many thousands of long-term patients have been released into the community, and considerable sums of money have been made available for community mental health. Community programs, however, have often used these funds for everything but long-term schizophrenic patients (Lamb and Edelson, 1976). Parents have often been appalled at the reluctance of local programs to fund aftercare projects that meet the needs of long-term patients and to pay for sheltered vocational workshops that offer patients an opportunity to be productive and increase their self-esteem. For too many community mental health programs, the tendency is to let these persons find their way into low-quality board-and-care homes, where they can again be forgotten just as they were in past days on the back wards of state hospitals.

Parents have found that even when their schizophrenic sons and daughters are accepted for treatment, they are often subsequently rejected from programs by staff members who say, "Our job is not to baby-sit for long-term patients." The problem often has to do with the patient's inability to participate verbally in a "satisfactory" way in group and individual therapy. What is often lacking is sufficient flexibility in the program, however, and tolerance and patience among the therapists to allow schizophrenics to remain in the program without having to do more than they can realistically do.

The Founding of Advocacy Groups

Because relatives have been unable to deal with these problems as individuals, advocacy organizations have sprung up. In England, the National Schizophrenia Fellowship was formed in 1972 and now has a membership of sixteen hundred families. The fellowship works to sponsor research into the cause of schizophrenia, spread a greater understanding of the special problems arising from the illness, secure the improvement of community care facilities of all kinds, and encourage patients and their families to help each other and themselves. The fellowship has members all over the United Kingdom and Ireland and has been instrumental in forming similar organizations in New Zealand, Australia, and West Germany. Similar organizations have been formed in Canada and Israel.

Parents of Adult Schizophrenics, a group located in San Mateo County, California, comprises more than two hundred families. There are thirty-seven similar organizations throughout California. In addition, there are two groups of relatives of patients currently in state hospitals. All belong to a statewide organization. Formal statewide organizations now exist in ten states and there are more than two hundred local organizations scattered about the nation. Moreover, there is now a national organization, the National Alliance for the Mentally Ill, headquartered in Washington with full-time staff.

Parents of Adult Schizophrenics was founded when a group of parents with schizophrenic children over eighteen years old got together and began comparing notes. They felt that they were receiving far more than their share of the blame for what had happened to their children and that no one in the professional ranks seemed to understand this or, for that matter, the problems inherent in being the parent of a schizophrenic. They wondered why parents of a child with leukemia were treated with sympathy and understanding, while parents of a child with schizophrenia received scorn and condemnation. They began to wonder if there was not more wrong with the system than with them.

Parents of Adult Schizophrenics began by sending a delegation to their local community mental health administrator to state what they saw as the needs of their schizophrenic sons and daughters. They were not exactly welcomed with open arms. They were told that if a community mental health staff were told to run such programs, the staff would say it was "nontherapeutic" and "just baby-sitting." The parents were doubly upset by such an attitude. For one thing, gearing a program to the level at which patients can function and grow is not baby-sitting. For another, are community mental health programs run for the benefit of the patients or the staff? The parents' suggestions were listened to politely, and sometimes not so politely, and then ignored.

But this was a persistent group. It became clear to them that they needed to be credible, knowledgeable, vocal, and highly visible. In terms of credibility, they are not wild-eyed radicals but typical representatives of middle America. They use every channel open to them to learn about mental health programs and administration, and many members of the organization now have a better overall knowledge of the mental health system than do some of the professionals who work in it. They went to see local politicians; they went to the newspapers. They had eight to ten people at every meeting of the local mental health advisory board. They lobbied to have all mental health programs studied and evaluated.

The members have discovered the importance of being political. Having begun with considerable naiveté, they now see how important it is to understand where the power is, not only in the mental health system but in the community generally, and what motivates and influences those in power. They have come to realize that having a role in financial deliberations and some control over the budget is a key to effective citizen participation (Yin and others, 1973).

Parents of Adult Schizophrenics has had considerable success. The members have influenced many programs by helping professionals change their attitudes toward parents. They have applied pressure and have been successful in having programs that serve long-term patients funded and expanded; in some cases, they have prevented these programs from being dismantled. They have obtained public money and grants from private foundations to establish a therapeutic housing program serving schizophrenic adults who have not been able to meet the expectations of other community therapeutic housing programs.

What Families Want and Need

Helpful advice on the practical management of schizophrenics is often difficult for relatives to obtain from professionals. Relatives do acquire considerable experience in coping with difficult behavior, however, usually through trial and error. In the words of John Wing (1977, p. 38), "Some learn not to argue with a deluded patient; others never learn. Some discover just how far they can go in trying to stimulate a rather slow and apathetic individual without arousing resentment. Others push too hard, find their efforts rejected or that they make matters worse, and then retreat into inactivity themselves. Some never give up intruding until the patient is driven away from home."

Mental health professionals often avoid the issue entirely when asked for advice (Creer and Wing, 1974)—and often the advice they do give is bad. Professionals thinking they are being empathic with the problems of relatives will advise, "If the patient behaves badly, throw him out and lock the door after him so he cannot get back in." This could be a dangerous course of action for the patient and a guilt-provoking act beyond the capabilities of the relative. Still another example: "Forget about him and live your life." Easy to say but difficult if not impossible to do when one feels guilt-ridden about a schizophrenic relative.

But there *is* practical advice that can be extremely helpful. The relatives' goals should be realistic; professionals and relatives should together determine what can realistically be achieved. Then, if objectivity can be maintained and emotional overinvolvement does not cloud the relatives' judgment, they can apply pressure to counteract the patient's social withdrawal, providing it does not push the patient toward standards beyond his capability and providing he is left a good deal of control over what he actually does. We have seen that many families can learn this by trial and error over a period of years but often only at great emotional cost that could have been avoided if they had been assisted by knowledgeable professionals. Relatives can be helped to see that although it is often useless to contradict delusional ideas, a patient can be told not to talk back to hallucinations in public. Relatives can be helped to understand that social withdrawal may be a necessary defense for schizophrenics but that too much withdrawal may lead to a form of institutionalism in the home; a balance must be struck.

A crucial time to deal sensitively with relatives is when the patient's first psychotic break occurs. (Professionals must also be aware of how the patient's illness can strain the marital relationship of the parents.) Relatives need to know that psychoses are not purely the result of "environmental factors," a term that parents take to mean *their* actions. It is helpful to point out that there are genetic and hereditary factors in the etiology of schizophrenia and that almost certainly a biochemical imbalance is involved. This information reduces the relatives' guilt, relieves them of their fears that by their actions they will drive their other children crazy, and makes them more willing to cooperate with the patient's treatment.

An Educational Approach

There is a growing consensus among those working with families of schizophrenics about the importance of an educational approach whereby professionals impart specific information and ways of dealing with mentally ill relatives. Usually families are explicitly told that there are no scientific data to suggest that schizophrenia is caused by childhood upbringing or family interactions (Falloon and others, 1981). Biochemical and genetic theories are outlined in a manner comprehensible to the families. Visual aids and clearly written handouts can be used to augment discussion.

There is now an increasing tendency to label the patient as someone with a serious illness (Anderson, Hogarty, and Reiss, 1981; Berkowitz and others, 1981). This is a controversial issue. The anti-labeling views of Laing and Szasz are well known. It is also the view of family therapists that labeling a patient as ill confines the problem to the patient, confers the sick role on him or her alone, and denies the family's role in the problem (Andolfi, 1979). Those espousing this new approach feel that labeling has advantages that outweigh its disadvantages. When a patient is behaving in a deeply disturbing way, the family is more likely to be able to help and support if they view the patient as ill rather than as hostile or lazy. The illness label also appears to reduce tendencies to attribute negative and emotional meanings to symptoms (Anderson, Hogarty, and Reiss, 1981). And as mentioned earlier, the family is not put off by the implication that the whole family is sick.

Because most patients are ambivalent about taking medication and because families can impede or facilitate this process, families are given information that may help them to support the medication regimen. Statistics are often given to demonstrate the high correlation between medication compliance and community tenure. The mechanisms of action, main effects, and possible side effects of antipsychotic medication, including tardive dyskinesia and weight gain, are given special attention. The use of anti-Parkinsonian agents is also explained along with the need for ongoing feedback about the effects of both types of drugs on the patient.

It is useful to emphasize to the family as well as to the patient that the illness includes a vulnerability to the interpersonal stresses common to everyday life. Goldstein and Kopeikin (1981) focus on helping the family identify the problems presenting the greatest threat to the patient's current and future stability. They then work with the family to develop strategies to avoid these stressful situations or, when the stressors cannot be avoided, to develop strategies to cope with them. This concrete, problem-focused, relatively simple format is particularly suited to the limited capacities of acute schizophrenics in the early stages of restitution. This approach is important because of the high relapse rate and stress of the first months after hospitalization. To improve the long-term benefits of therapy, treatment should probably progress beyond this focus on crisis and the management of imminent stresses.

Relatives should be told not to be at the patient's beck and call (Berkowitz and others, 1981). The family is told implicitly or explicitly that they should begin to lead an independent and satisfying life and that being self-sacrificing is counterproductive. Families are also encouraged to pay a normal amount of attention to the needs of other family members (Anderson, Hogarty, and Reiss,

1981). Failure to do so is likely to deplete family resources and make long-term support of the patient increasingly difficult. Parallels are drawn between the course of schizophrenia and other chronic illnesses, such as diabetes, in which patients and families must learn ongoing management techniques and methods of living with the illness without allowing its symptoms to dominate their lives.

Anderson, Hogarty, and Reiss (1981) emphasize the schizophrenic's sensitivity to environmental stimulation. These patients seem to have cognitive deficits that make it difficult for them to process and respond to even normal amounts of environmental stimuli. Families are given ways in which they can create barriers to overstimulation by setting reasonable limits, having realistic goals, and allowing for interpersonal distance without rejection. In general, the family is encouraged to set limits on unreasonable, bizarre behavior before tension builds or blowups occur. The need for limits is stressed because many families feel that, since the patient is sick, he or she cannot be asked or expected to perform on any level. Creating a low-key environment does not mean creating a permissive one; when one is disorganized, structure is reassuring.

Families are encouraged to respect interpersonal boundaries in concrete ways—allowing family members to speak for themselves, permitting family members to do things separately, and recognizing each other's limitations and vulnerabilities. Both patient and family are helped to see that the need for distance relates to survival and does not constitute rejection. A family routine is encouraged that includes "time outs," thereby allowing the patient or other family members to retreat to their rooms or go for a walk when feelings of agitation or overstimulation arise. Furthermore, patient and family are asked to discuss and agree on signals that indicate the need for psychological space and the need for support.

Talking to Families

Kanter (1980) advises relatives not to fight battles they cannot win. The patient, having seen his relatives fail in repeated attempts to change the family situation, begins to perceive them as weak and ineffectual. In Kanter's words (p. 12): "Once this image of his relative as ineffectual has developed, the disturbed person may treat his family members like the boy who cried wolf, ignoring successive attempts to change."

In talking with families, Kanter (pp. 12-13) discusses what he considers one of the central problems:

> To implement an effective structure in your relations with your troubled relatives, I believe the first place to start is with the matter of your own self-preservation. I cite the first rule of lifesaving: Don't let the drowning victim take you, the lifeguard, with him. If you are exhausted and intimidated, you will be of little value to your relative. Don't tolerate a climate of fear and possible violence. I advise taking whatever measures are necessary to physically protect yourself. Do not hesitate to call your family or friends for help should your troubled relatives become aggressive. If necessary, call the police. If you want a prompt response, don't report a long story over the phone. Just tell them there is an assault in progress. You can decide later whether to press charges or obtain a petition for commitment. Such occasions are no time for negotiation or understanding; productive dialogue can only occur when everyone is relatively free to speak their mind. In my experience, many family members live in a state of continual though subtle intimidation. The patient suggests he or she will remain in control of their aggressive impulses as long as . . . relatives overlook some important sources of discomfort. If this is the case in your family, I would suggest taking a close look at how this situation can be altered. Little progress can be made in a climate of fear.
>
> Once you have successfully negotiated setting limits on aggressive and intimidating behavior, I advise taking a closer look at whether you really have control over your household and family affairs. In other words, can you live comfortably in your own home? Does your troubled relative barge in on you whenever he or she feels like it? Do they have personal habits which threaten the safety of the family such as carelessness with cigarettes? Do they keep you awake with strange hours or loud music? Do they clean up after themselves? Do they help with the household chores? Do they let you know when they will be home for meals? Does your relative drain your financial resources? Does he give you an opportunity to enjoy some solitude? To sum up, does your disturbed relative treat you with the respect and consideration you would expect from a house guest? If not, these questions may suggest areas of concern that might be productively ad-

dressed, as they are all matters where the patient's behavior impinges on your life.

When I suggest focusing on these sort of problems, family members often argue that these matters, though irritating, are relatively tolerable. Instead, they are more concerned that their troubled relative move into a halfway house or get a job. While I agree that these larger goals are important, I believe that the disturbed person who has trouble treating his family with consideration and respect will also tend to have serious problems in other life situations. I would also suggest that these larger goals may be battles that the family cannot easily win. I really don't know how to make someone get a job who doesn't want to work. On the other hand, I see coping with a relative's noise or sloppiness as a more manageable problem where family members can enjoy a greater degree of success. Also, I believe that it is difficult to help one's disturbed relative until one has control over one's own environment. I see this notion as equally valuable for professionals. For instance, in my clinic work, I deal promptly and firmly with clients who annoy our receptionist or others in the waiting room. I have found that high expectations in these mundane areas of living generally pay rich dividends in the long run.

Other Help for Families and Patients

In some instances assertiveness training helps relatives set limits on the schizophrenic's behavior; at times it also helps parents deal more effectively with professionals. In some cases, of course, the relatives are already too assertive; if so, professionals should work with them tactfully to lessen their assertiveness or channel it into activities such as advocacy for increased and better-quality services for their schizophrenic relatives. Adequate treatment and rehabilitative services are needed to help relatives care for the schizophrenic. Without these services the family may have all it can do simply to cope with the patient, much less treat and rehabilitate him, and here too the situation can easily deteriorate into a form of institutionalism at home.

A whole range of facilities are needed with all degrees of structure for those patients who need out-of-home placement. Otherwise, the schizophrenic may be unwilling and the parents too guilt-ridden to effect the separation. An especially difficult problem is the schizophrenic who also has an alcohol or drug problem. Such patients will probably need a highly structured program with intensive supervision, monitoring of their activities and their comings and goings, and the power to restrict them if they cannot handle their freedom. Other patients need a less structured but highly nurturing facility. Also important are professionals who can discriminate and decide who needs what kind of facility.

Many families can manage their schizophrenic relatives well if they have access to periodic respite care so that they can take a "vacation" from the hard work of coping with a schizophrenic. This is true not only for parents but for siblings, who frequently are neglected in the midst of the family's preoccupation with taking care of the schizophrenic.

It is essential that relatives' organizations maintain their separate identities. There have been instances when leaders have been appointed to mental health advisory boards or positions of responsibility in mental health associations and then invested most of their time and energy in these positions. Though this has in one sense been very positive, an unfortunate result has been that the relatives' organizations have collapsed, leaving the community without an independent, effective peer organization and advocacy group for patients and their relatives.

Parents of Adult Schizophrenics also takes into account the needs of its own members. There is a monthly "woe night" when all parents of adult schizophrenics are welcome to come and talk about their problems and their feelings. These gatherings provide therapeutic ventilation and peer support. Parents have been helped through crises, and further emotional breakdown has thus been averted in both individuals and families.

The organization has helped many of its members feel less isolated. Subtle changes occur in friendships when one family has a schizophrenic child. Friends hesitate to talk about the accomplishments of their own children and do not know whether to discuss the illness or avoid the subject. The friendship becomes strained; former friends see less and less of each other. Within the organization, parents find others who have similar problems and with whom they can talk openly. Families that have become isolated can reestablish a social life.

Parents' organizations often begin with a concern about the members' own children and then grow into a determination to do something about the entire problem of community treatment and rehabilitation for long-term schizophrenics. As a result, there now exist an increasing number of effective parents' groups devoted to advocacy of the needs and rights of these patients.

Accountability—Not Control

Consumer groups such as Parents of Adult Schizophrenics are frequently seen as "too outspoken" and "too aggressive," probably because they do speak up, just as minority groups and women's groups have had to do in order to be heard. The latter, too, were not well received at first, though many mental health professionals were sympathetic to their causes. But these groups, unlike parents' groups, were not seen as threatening in the sense of questioning the theories, actions, expertise, and priorities of mental health professionals and service programs.

Community mental health is still in the throes of learning how to integrate consumerism and parent advocacy in its philosophy and everyday operations. Mental health professionals should regard concerned parents' groups as partners in the quest for better human services (Wolfensberger, 1972), rather than as nuisances or adversaries to professionalism generally and their agencies in particular. Though citizen groups may take issue with public and private agencies, *responsible* groups do not usually interfere with an agency's functioning unless it fails to meet important community needs (Moise, 1975).

One factor influencing the growth of consumerism has been the increasing recognition that human services to those who need them are not a privilege but a right (Lourie, 1975; Wolfensberger, 1972). From this point of view, it is essential to have input from people in the community—and not just from docile citizens who echo the professionals' positions and give the appearance of community participation. Although professionals may lose some of their control, generally the issue is more one of community accountability than of community control (Schiff, 1970). Accountability to users has been described as the critical ingredient of citizen participation (Roman and Schmais, 1972). Although some groups of paraprofessionals and some citizens groups have demanded control, most *responsible* organizations (exemplified by parents' groups) have demanded accountability from public and private programs. These parents' groups, as exemplified by the National Schizophrenia Fellowship and Parents of Adult Schizophrenics, are concerned primarily that essential services are provided, that they are available to those who need them when they are needed, and that they are appropriate and of good quality.

A Final Word

Families of schizophrenics have received too little help from mental health professionals, even though in many cases families are the real primary care agents for long-term, severely disabled patients. Some of the problems that arise in living with a long-term patient have been described in this chapter, as well as mutual-support and advocacy groups formed by relatives. Mental health professionals can help families of schizophrenics by providing practical, realistic advice on how to deal with the illness, by offering empathy and support rather than placing blame, and by working to ensure that treatment and rehabilitation services are not only available but adequate.

❧ Nine ❧

The Mentally Ill in Jail

In the wake of deinstitutionalization, there has been increasing concern about the chronically and severely mentally ill population in a variety of community settings. That concern rightfully extends to the sizable number of persons with severe psychiatric problems who enter the criminal justice system. This chapter examines some of the interactions between these patients, now out in the community in such large numbers, and the criminal justice system.

Several studies describe a "criminalization" of mentally disordered behavior (Abramson, 1972; Urmer, 1971)—that is, a shunting of mentally ill persons in need of treatment into the criminal justice system instead of the mental health system. Rather than hospitalization and psychiatric treatment, the mentally ill are said to be subject to inappropriate arrest and incarceration. Certainly deinstitutionalization has led to large numbers of the mentally ill in the community; at the same time, there is a limited amount of community psychiatric resources, including hospital beds. The result is pressure to institutionalize persons needing twenty-four-hour care wherever there is room—including jail. Legal restrictions placed on involuntary hospitalization are also said to result in a diversion of

Note: This chapter is a revised version of a paper by the author and Robert W. Grant entitled "The Mentally Ill in an Urban County Jail," *Archives of General Psychiatry,* 1982, *39* (1), 17–22.

some patients to the criminal justice system (Abramson, 1972; Rock, Jacobson, and Janotaul, 1968).

To what extent do county jail inmates have diagnosable mental illness? The Bolton study (Arthur Bolton Associates, 1976) found that in a five-county, combined sample of 1,084 adults in California county jails, 6.7 percent were psychotic and 9.3 percent were judged to have nonpsychotic mental disorders, not including personality disorders. For Los Angeles County, the figures were 7.8 percent psychotic and 5.7 percent nonpsychotic. In another study in Denver of a random sample of 100 newly arrived county jail inmates, 3 percent were found to be functionally psychotic and 2 percent organically psychotic (Swank and Winer, 1976). In a random sample of 174 inmates of the Oklahoma state prison system, 5.2 percent were found to be psychotic (James and others, 1980). Considerable doubt was expressed in the Bolton study, and by others (Steadman and Ribner, 1980), that the number of mentally ill persons in jail has increased; rather, it was suggested that they may now simply be recognized to a greater extent than before. Clearly, further study is needed of the mentally disordered jail population.

This chapter begins with a study of the mentally ill in an urban county jail and then goes on to discuss how these patients are perceived by the police, whether in fact there has been criminalization of the mentally ill, and what changes need to be made to alleviate the problems of these patients. The study, conducted in 1980–1981, concentrated on male inmates in the Los Angeles County Jail who were referred by the jail custody staff for psychiatric evaluation. My colleague and I sought answers to the following questions: What are the characteristics of the population—demographic findings, living situation before arrest, work history, mental status, diagnosis? To what extent in the past have they been involved in the criminal justice system, the mental health system, or both? Why were these persons booked into jail rather than admitted to a psychiatric hospital? Are there problems for this group that can be traced to the overall philosophy and implementation of community treatment?

Method

We worked as part-time members (one day a week) of the Forensic Mental Health Unit in the Los Angeles County Central

Men's Jail, where we performed psychiatric evaluations. This unit routinely evaluates inmates thought by the jail staff at the initial jail screening or at any other time during incarceration to have current psychiatric problems. Evaluations were done on 102 inmates selected at random from among those referred for psychiatric evaluation. Patients were excluded from the study if their primary problem was alcoholism, phencyclidine intoxication, drug addiction, or developmental disability.

We conducted the full psychiatric evaluations, filled out the required Forensic Mental Health Unit forms, and made all appropriate psychiatric referrals and dispositions, including hospitalization. The information we gathered in these evaluations comprised a psychiatric diagnosis (DSM-III), a psychiatric history, a work history, a history of prior arrests, a history of community residential placements such as board-and-care homes, and accounts from the inmates as to how they saw their lives. We consulted previous psychiatric records of the unit and read police reports when available (48 of the 102 cases). We also made direct contact with the police in the course of the evaluations in eight cases. We attempted to reach the family by phone and involve them in the disposition if possible; often we obtained additional information in the process. (Confidentiality of patient records in the Forensic Mental Health Unit is protected by the Lanterman-Petris-Short Act, as in all mental health agencies in California.)

The inmates we evaluated had already been screened informally at several levels. The first screening takes place at the point of arrest, when the police determine that the person has committed a crime and should be taken to jail instead of a hospital. The second screening takes place at arraignment, when the judge may decide that the primary problem is probably not the alleged offense (in most cases misdemeanors) but basically a psychiatric problem. In such cases, the judge has the option to ask a mental health staff member to examine the defendant to determine whether he meets the criteria for involuntary hospitalization in California—namely, if he is a danger to himself or others or is gravely disabled. If he meets these criteria, a seventy-two-hour observation period at a psychiatric hospital is initiated. If the person does not meet these criteria for involuntary hospitalization and refuses voluntary hospitalization or is judged not to need it, he is returned to the court for further proceedings or release from custody if the judge believes the alleged offense was too minor to warrant further time in jail. Members of our sample had gone through both screening processes and had not been directed into the mental health service system.

Setting

The Los Angeles County Central Men's Jail has an average daily census of 5,500 men. There are 155,000 bookings per year (not an unduplicated count). The Forensic Mental Health Unit, where we worked, receives approximately 5,400 referrals a year, or approximately 4.5 percent of all persons booked into the jail when multiple bookings of the same person are taken into account. The great majority of persons referred to the Forensic Mental Health Unit are psychotic (98 percent in this study). As mentioned earlier, in the Bolton study (1976) 7.8 percent of a random sample of Los Angeles County inmates were given psychotic diagnoses.

Results

This was a relatively young population, with a median age of 29.5 years and a range of 18 to 79 years. The study was conducted on an all-male population. Of the 102 inmates, 49 (48 percent) were white, 43 (42 percent) were black, and 10 (10 percent) were Mexican-American. Moreover, 67 (66 percent) had never been married, 25 (25 percent) were divorced or separated, 8 (8 percent) were married, and 2 (2 percent) were widowed. The subjects' median education was eleventh grade, ranging from no formal schooling to a master's degree. Of 102 subjects, 76 (75 percent) were diagnosed by the investigators (DSM-III) as having schizophrenia, 22 (22 percent) major affective disorder, 2 (2 percent) organic brain syndrome, and 2 (2 percent) adjustment disorders.

As for source of support, 57 (56 percent) were receiving Supplemental Security Income, 21 (21 percent) had no source of support, 12 (12 percent) supported themselves through employment, 3 (3 percent) were supported by their parents, 3 (3 percent) were receiving general (county) relief, 1 (1 percent) had a full Veterans

Administration pension, 1 (1 percent) was receiving unemployment insurance, 1 (1 percent) received retirement benefits, 1 (1 percent) received state disability benefits, and 1 (1 percent) described his source of support as selling narcotics and another (1 percent) as pimping.

At the time of arrest, 30 (29 percent) were living with parents, 7 (7 percent) with other relatives, 8 (8 percent) with wives or girl-friends, 2 (2 percent) with friends, and 8 (8 percent) in board-and-care homes. Some 37 (36 percent) were living as transients; 26 (25 percent) were living on the streets, on the beach, in their cars, or in missions, and another 11 (11 percent) in cheap hotels. Nine (9 percent) were otherwise living alone. One (1 percent) had been in a state hospital and was brought to jail after seriously assaulting a staff member.

Of the 102 inmates, 92 (90 percent) had a history of psychiatric hospitalization. Many had been in multiple inpatient settings; thus 82 (80 percent) had been hospitalized at a state hospital, 24 (24 percent) had been confined in hospitals for the criminally insane, and 41 (40 percent) had been in various other institutions such as county, private, and Veterans Administration hospitals and psychiatric wards in general hospitals. Fourteen inmates (14 percent) were receiving some form of mental health treatment (primarily medication only) at the point of arrest. Only 25 (25 percent) altogether had received any form of outpatient mental health treatment at any time in their lives.

Criminal charges on which the inmates were booked on this arrest are given in Table 2. Fifty-three inmates (52 percent) were charged with felonies; of these, approximately half were crimes of violence. Forty-two crimes (41 percent) were misdemeanors; of these, 13 (31 percent) were assault and battery. The remaining 7 inmates (7 percent) had been brought to jail because of outstanding bench warrants. Overall, 40 (39 percent) of the 102 inmates were charged with violent crimes.

There was a relationship between the seriousness of the criminal charge and the living situation just prior to arrest (Table 3). Fifty-one percent of those charged with misdemeanors had been living on the streets or on the beach or in missions and cheap hotels, compared with 23 percent of those charged with felonies.

Table 2. Criminal Charges of the 102 Inmates
Referred for Psychiatric Evaluation.

Criminal Charge	Number of Subjects
Felonies	
Armed robbery[a]	9
Assault with deadly weapon[a]	8
Murder[a]	4
Assault on peace officer[a]	2
Felony assault[a]	2
Rape[a]	2
Burglary	11
Grand theft and grand theft auto	7
Felony drug	3
Forgery	1
Concealed weapon	1
Threats to kill parole officer	1
Arson	1
Lewd act with child under 14	1
Total	53
Misdemeanors	
Assault and battery[a]	13
Malicious mischief	7
Disorderly conduct under influence of alcohol or drugs	5
Petty theft	4
Loitering	3
Drunk driving	3
Disturbing the peace	2
Misdemeanor drug	2
Defrauding an innkeeper	1
Auto tampering	1
Disrupting a school	1
Reckless driving	1
Total	43
Outstanding bench warrants	6

[a]Crimes of violence.

Seventy-seven (75 percent) had prior felony arrests. Seventeen (17 percent) had prior arrests for misdemeanors only; 8 (8 percent) had no prior arrests.

To assess psychopathology, we used the five-point psychiatric assessment scales developed by Krawiecka, Goldberg, and

Table 3. Seriousness of Criminal Charge
and Living Situation.

Criminal Charge	Living on Streets or Beach or in Missions and Cheap Hotels N (%)	All Other Living Situations N (%)	Total N (%)
Misdemeanors[a]	25 (51)	24 (49)	49 (100)
Felonies	12 (23)	41 (77)	53 (100)
Total	37	65	102

Note: P < 0.01.
[a]Includes outstanding bench warrants.

Vaughan (1977). The presence of severe, overt psychopathology was defined here as the manifestation of major or severe symptoms in at least two of the following three scales: delusions, hallucinations, and thought disorder (incoherence and irrelevance of speech). Using this definition, 82 (80 percent) of the sample exhibited severe, overt major psychopathology.

Eighty inmates (78 percent) had histories of serious physical violence against others, ranging from assault to murder. Table 4 shows a relationship between violence and severe overt psychopathology; 85 percent of those with a history of serious physical violence were found to have severe, overt psychopathology, compared with 64 percent of those with no history of serious physical violence.

Forty-three inmates (42 percent) had a history of residence in a board-and-care home. Table 5 demonstrates the relationship between such residence and age; only 11 percent of those under the age of twenty-seven had ever resided in a board-and-care home, compared with 53 percent of those twenty-seven years of age and older.

Sixty-seven inmates (66 percent) had held at least one job for six months or longer. Only 5 (5 percent) had ever been under conservatorship (a legal status established in California by the Lanterman-Petris-Short Act). The conservator has the power to place the patient involuntarily in a hospital or a residential community setting, unlocked or locked depending upon the patient's needs, and to manage the patient's money.

The evaluations in this study resulted in recommendations for psychiatric hospitalization for 77 persons (76 percent).

Table 4. History of Serious Physical Violence
and Severe Overt Psychopathology.

History of Serious Physical Violence Against Persons	Severe Overt Psychopathology[a]		
	Yes (%) N (%)	No (%) N (%)	Total (%) N (%)
Yes	68 (85)	12 (15)	80 (100)
No	14 (64)	8 (36)	22 (100)
Total	82	20	102

[a]$P < 0.05$.

Determining why some of the inmates had been arrested proved difficult. There was no doubt concerning the 53 (52 percent) charged with felonies and the 7 (7 percent) with outstanding bench warrants, for whom jail was routine regardless of mental status. The uncertain cases were mostly those charged with misdemeanors, for whom presumably the police often have some discretion in choosing psychiatric hospitalization versus jail. In some instances, the person was apparently brought to jail because of a citizen's arrest and insistence by the citizen that the person be taken to jail. In other cases, the person may not have been clearly mentally ill at the time of arrest. Still another factor that may have influenced the decision in a number of these cases is the difficulty police experience in trying to obtain hospitalization for those they consider mentally ill. These and other factors are fully discussed in the next section. In many cases of persons charged with misdemeanors, it was possible to determine which of these factors had caused the person to be arrested rather than hospitalized, but in others it was impossible to make a reliable judgment. In some cases it seemed to be a combination of factors. Therefore, classification could be made with certainty with regard to reason for arrest, as opposed to hospitalization, only into the three broad categories of charges—felonies (52 percent), outstanding bench warrants (7 percent), and misdemeanors (41 percent)—without trying to subclassify misdemeanor arrests.

Comment

This was a study of 102 male inmates in a large urban county jail who had been referred for psychiatric evaluation. Ninety percent

Table 5. Past Residence in Board-and-Care Homes and Age.

| Past Residence in Board-and-Care Home | Age (Years)[a] | | Total |
	< 27 (%) N (%)	≥ 27 (%) N (%)	
Yes	3 (11)	40 (53)	43
No	24 (89)	35 (47)	59
Total	27 (100)	75 (100)	102

[a]$P < 0.001$.

had a history of psychiatric hospitalizations. (Four fifths had been in state hospitals and one fourth in hospitals for the criminally insane.) Some 92 percent had a prior arrest record, 75 percent with at least one prior felony arrest. Four fifths exhibited severe, overt major psychopathology. Three fourths were diagnosed as having schizophrenia and almost one fourth as having major affective disorders. As a result of the evaluation, psychiatric hospitalization was recommended for more than three fourths (76 percent); that is, we judged them to meet the criteria for involuntary hospitalization: dangerous to self or others or gravely disabled (unable, as a result of mental disorder, to provide for their personal needs for food, clothing, and shelter). More than one third had been living, at the point of arrest, on the streets, on the beach, or in missions or cheap hotels. Only 12 percent had been supporting themselves through employment at the time of arrest. Thus, it is clear that this population had had extensive experience with both the criminal justice and mental health systems; it was characterized, moreover, by severe acute and chronic mental illness and generally functioned at a low level.

With regard to criminal charges on this arrest, more than half were charged with felonies and more than half of these were crimes of violence. Thirty-one percent of the misdemeanors were assault and battery, which is consistent with the finding of Whitmer (1980) who noted that many young male paranoid schizophrenics are arrested for assault.

More than half of those charged with misdemeanors had been living on the streets or on the beach or in missions or cheap hotels, compared with less than a fourth of those charged with felonies. While we have no data that would further interpret this finding, we can speculate on some possible explanations. Persons living in such places obviously have a minimum of community support. Perhaps the less serious misdemeanor offense is frequently a way of asking for help. Moreover, it may be that many of this group of uncared-for mentally ill persons are being arrested for minor criminal acts that are really manifestations of their illness, their lack of treatment, and the absence of structure in their lives. Certainly these were our clinical impressions as we talked to these inmates and read the police reports. I should add, however, that there were some inmates, even though overtly psychotic, whose underlying antisocial character problems appeared to play a major role as causative factors for their alleged criminal behavior.

We were struck by the large proportion (78 percent) of the sample who had histories of serious physical violence ranging from assault to murder. The relationship between history of serious physical violence against others and severe overt psychopathology suggests that at least some of this violence may represent a psychotic loss of control in these persons—again consistent with our clinical impressions.

There is a striking difference in the percentage of those under twenty-seven years of age with a history of residence in a board-and-care home and the much higher percentage of those over twenty-seven. The older one is, the more opportunity one has had to live in different situations, including board-and-care homes. In our conversations with these men about such facilities, other patterns emerged: the tendency of the young mentally ill to hold out for autonomy rather than living in a protected and supervised setting and the tendency to resist both entering the mental health system and being labeled as a psychiatric patient, even to the extent of living in a board-and-care home.

A large number of these young inmates had had board-and-care homes recommended to them repeatedly as part of their hospital discharge plans but had consistently refused to go to them. It appeared to us that eventually many of these persons gave up the struggle, at least temporarily, and accepted board-and-care home placement. It should be noted, however, that most of them had left their board-and-care homes after relatively brief periods. It was our clinical impression that in some cases this living situation was not sufficiently structured for them. In other cases, what came across to us as these men spoke was a desire to regain their autonomy, their isolated life-style, and their freedom to engage in antisocial activities. Although a high proportion of this population had serious psychiatric problems, only eight were living in board-and-care homes at the point of arrest.

Jail Versus Hospital. Determining why an inmate had been arrested rather than taken to a hospital was not a simple matter. In many cases, of course, it was clear why the person had been arrested. For instance, almost everyone who is thought to have committed a felony is arrested and taken to jail, regardless of mental condition. This group comprised more than half the population studied. The criminal justice system, charged by society with the responsibility for removing from the community persons charged with serious crimes, sees no alternative but to place the person charged with a felony in custody in a secure setting and then arrange for psychiatric treatment if necessary. If the accused is thought to have committed a serious crime, the police and the criminal justice system generally do not want to leave this person in the hands of a psychiatric hospital where security may be lax, where the offense may be seen as secondary to the patient's illness, and where the person may be released by the hospital back to the community after a relatively short period of time. Persons with outstanding bench warrants, usually for failure to appear in court for traffic infractions, are also routinely brought to jail regardless of other circumstances. This group constituted 7 percent of the sample.

It is when we come to those charged with misdemeanors (41 percent of the sample) that the question becomes more complex. A person who appears mentally ill to a mental health professional may not give the same impression to a police officer, who despite a wealth of practical experience is still essentially a layman in these matters. Some mentally ill persons prefer to see themselves as criminals rather than as "crazy" and present themselves accordingly (Sadoff, 1971).

Moreover, mental illness may appear to the police as alcohol or drug intoxication, especially if the person has been using drugs or alcohol at the time of arrest. And in the heat and confusion of an encounter with the police and other citizens, which may include subduing the person by force, signs of mental illness may go unnoticed. As one policeman put it after a difficult arrest, "He didn't look any more mentally disturbed than any other criminal."

The demands of citizens are yet another factor. Many stores have a policy that *anyone* caught shoplifting should go to jail, and store managers are instructed to make a citizen's arrest and call the police, without exception. Similarly, the management of the bus station, located in the midst of what is now skid row, wants to discourage people from trying to live there or harass or beg from passengers. In their brief and sometimes not too friendly interactions with "suspect" individuals, security guards often are unable to differentiate mental illness from alcoholism and the character problems of many of the denizens of the neighborhood. In still another kind of situation, the person who has just been assaulted by a psychotic patient is often disinclined to be sympathetic to the assailant's mental status even when the mental disturbance is evident. Thus, an angry citizen may insist on signing a citizen's arrest and having the person taken to jail.

Another crucial factor is the age-old conflict between the police and emergency room physicians, a problem that is made worse by a shortage of psychiatric beds. The police complain, often with justification, that they are made to wait with their prospective patients for inordinate periods of time in emergency rooms and are thus taken out of service. Even then, they may finally be told (after the person is examined) that there are no beds available and thus the police still have responsibility for the person. Or they may leave the person in the hospital (the person who just a short time before constituted a clear menace to the community) and later find that the emergency room psychiatrist has ignored their judgment and released the person back to the community.

There is considerable merit to the complaints of the police. The public hospital clinician, faced with the daily realities of crowding, inadequate staffing and facilities, and an increasing volume of paperwork, will try to avoid admission to the hospital (Bassuk and Schoonover, 1981). Because of this, many policemen do not want to take the accused to a hospital. Moreover, they are often not inclined to talk a citizen out of a citizen's arrest. Or, in the case of a person who has committed a misdemeanor but is clearly mentally ill, the police may well book the person into jail—which is less time consuming and ensures the person's removal from the community pending further evaluation—rather than take him to a hospital. Furthermore, the police often do not know whether an uncooperative person will meet the criteria for involuntary hospitalization; if they consider the person a danger to society, jail is a more reliable way to take that person out of circulation, at least temporarily (Abramson, 1972). In still other instances, the mental disturbance is recognized by the police but, as one policeman told us, "He seemed crazy, but he knew right from wrong in regard to this offense and we felt he should go to jail." It should not be forgotten that the police see their prime responsibility as protecting society whereas psychiatrists are often ambivalent about whether they are primarily responsible to the individual or to society.

A study in Pennsylvania found that mental illness-related incidents coming to the attention of the police increased 227.6 percent from 1975 to 1979 (Bonovitz and Bonovitz, 1981). It should be emphasized that the police have been left with the responsibility of dealing with these aspects of mental illness and crime and violence in an informal "common-sense" way without any formal mandate to do so or development of a formal policy.

Has There Been Criminalization of the Mentally Ill? Society has a limited tolerance of mentally disordered behavior (Rachlin, Pam, and Milton, 1975). This is especially true for those who have *direct* contact with the mentally ill—namely the courts, professionals, families, and other citizens (Lamb, Sorkin, and Zusman, 1981). Many believe that if the entry of persons exhibiting disturbed behavior into the mental health system of social control is impeded, community pressure will result in at least partial circumvention of the obstacles, legal or otherwise, or will force some of these persons into the criminal justice system of social control (Rock, Jacobson, and Janotaul, 1968).

There has been considerable discussion of the "criminalization" of the mentally ill over the past decade. It is said that many of the mentally ill who would formerly have been treated in mental hospitals are being forced into the penal system by changes in com-

mitment laws, shortages of hospital beds, and deinstitutionalization. There are those (Steadman and Ribner, 1980; Arthur Bolton
Associates, 1976) who say instead that persons who have committed
criminal acts and are mentally ill have always been found in jail in
large numbers—that there is simply greater recognition and identification of them now. Unfortunately, there are no good studies
spanning the periods before and after deinstitutionalization that
would allow us to put the current situation into perspective.

There are, however, data suggesting a diversion of patients
into the criminal justice system. Abramson (1972) showed that following the enactment of the Lanterman-Petris-Short Act in California, which eliminated indefinite commitment and made many
far-reaching changes in the procedures for securing involuntary
hospitalization, there was an increasing resort to criminal procedures to secure long-term indefinite commitment by raising the
issue of competence to stand trial regardless of the severity of the
"offense" if the patient's behavior was sufficiently disturbed or
disturbing.

Studies in recent years have shown that the arrest rates for
ex-hospital patients are higher than those for the general population (Zitrin, Hardesty, and Burdock, 1976; Sosowsky, 1978; Steadman, Vanderwyst, and Ribner, 1978). There have been various
attempts to account for these increased arrest rates. Steadman and
others (1978) concluded from their data that the increase is due almost entirely to the greater number of persons with arrest records
who are being admitted to mental hospitals. Sosowsky (1980), however, has shown that ex-hospital patients from a California county
with *no* previous arrests were arrested roughly three times more
often than the general county population and five times more often
for serious violent crimes. Grunberg, Klinger, and Grument (1977)
have suggested that more liberty for the traditional hospital patient
is likely a crucial factor in explaining the observed increase. As
Sosowsky (1978, p. 42) has noted, "It may be true that the mentally
ill, traditionally treated in state hospitals, are more violent than the
general public and that more liberty does result in more crime and
violence." Thus, it seems possible that mental status as such is cau-
sally related to the increased arrest rate and that those who would

have been hospitalized before deinstitutionalization are now in the community and more subject to arrest.

What Can Be Done? Clearly the system of voluntary mental health outpatient treatment is inadequate for this population, who are, moreover, extremely resistant to it. If they do agree to accept treatment, they tend not to keep their appointments, not to take their medications, and to be least welcome at outpatient facilities (Whitmer, 1980). This pattern is confirmed by our findings, which show only 14 percent receiving any form of outpatient treatment, even including those receiving only medication, at the point of arrest and only 25 percent who had ever been receiving outpatient treatment at any time.

There needs to be much more emphasis on ongoing involuntary treatment for persons like those in this study. Social controls are important not only for society but also for these patients, for whom life without structure and controls is chaotic and characterized by intense anxiety, depression, fear, and deprivation. Certainly, these were our clinical impressions of the men we evaluated in this study.

There are several areas on which we can focus, at least initially, in providing therapeutic social controls for the mentally ill who lack the internal controls to manage their own lives. To begin with, jails are often better equipped than hospitals to handle violent patients. The staff of the county jail where we worked was better trained and more disciplined than any mental health staff we have seen to manage violent patients in a humane way, and the physical setup was suited to the task. Most hospitals have a good deal to learn in this regard.

It was our belief in evaluating the men in this study that (1) the pendulum should begin to swing back with regard to laws pertaining to involuntary treatment so that those who need it can receive it and that (2) little use is made of the legal provisions already available. In California conservatorship is perhaps the most obvious example. In our opinion, a large proportion of the inmates we examined were chronically gravely disabled. Yet only 5 percent had ever been under conservatorship. Conservatorship provides continuous control and monitoring of patients who need social controls while at the same time retaining adequate legal safeguards. Under conservatorship, granted by the court for one-year renewable periods, patients can be hospitalized when necessary and for an indefinite period, their money can be managed when they cannot do it for themselves, and they can be compelled to live in a suitable residential facility in the community that meets their needs for care and structure—a facility such as a board-and-care home or, when needed, a locked skilled-nursing facility (see Chapter Six).

Why is greater use not made of conservatorship? Bureaucratic obstacles and the inertia of the system are among the greatest problems, even when mental health professionals recognize the need for ongoing controls in the community. The inmates we studied are an extremely difficult group to control, let alone treat. Crisis services and voluntary outpatient treatment are a vital beginning. What is needed, however, is an all-out effort with sufficient funding to provide adequate ongoing community treatment services, both outpatient and residential, to this group.

This effort will need to adopt a treatment philosophy that external controls, such as conservatorship, can be a positive and often crucial therapeutic modality for those who lack the internal controls to deal with their impulses and to organize themselves to cope with life's demands. In such cases we can, for instance, interrupt a self-destructive life on the streets frequently interspersed with crises, hospitalization, and time in jail. There must also be pressure on government agencies that serve as public guardians to implement these recommendations promptly. We can then hope to begin to interrupt this continual pattern of jail and hospital and help these persons achieve some measure of order and security in their lives.

A Final Word

From all that I have observed, the lives of a large proportion of these inmates are characterized by chaos, dysphoria, and deprivation as they try to survive in a world for which they are ill prepared. They cry out for control and structure, as do their families and neighbors, but who listens or wants to believe?

⁓ Ten ⁓

Individual
Psychotherapy

With the emptying of state hospitals, mental health professionals are being called on to provide community treatment to increasingly large numbers of long-term, severely disabled patients. Individual psychotherapy is often dismissed, if it is thought of at all, when professionals plan community programs for these patients. Individual psychotherapy, however, can play a central role, but first there must be a clearly understood point of view and rationale so that potential therapists do not turn away from the task in confusion and dismay. Long-term patients were seen—and saw themselves—as helpless and incompetent in the state hospital. It is important not to dismiss them, in the same way, as being incapable of using psychotherapy.

Above all, we should direct our efforts to giving patients a sense of mastery (Fenichel, 1946)—the feeling that they can cope with their internal drives, their symptoms, and the demands of their environment. With the development of mastery, patients achieve not only a better adaptation to their world but also a significant rise in self-esteem. To attain our object, we need to work with the *well* part of the ego. Regardless of the degree of psychopathology in evidence, there is always an intact portion of the ego to which treatment and

Note: This is a revised and expanded version of a chapter by the author from H. R. Lamb and Associates, *Community Survival for Long-Term Patients* (San Francisco: Jossey-Bass, 1976).

121

rehabilitation efforts can be directed (Lamb, 1971b). The goal, then, is to expand the remaining well part of the person and thus his functioning rather than to remove or cure pathology; the focus should be on the *healthy* part of the personality and the person's *strengths*.

The trend in the psychotherapy of schizophrenia in particular has been toward a decreasing interest in psychopathology and a growing interest in practical issues of adaptation (Gunderson, 1973). The point of view expressed in this chapter is consistent with this trend. It focuses on reality rather than fantasy, on the present and the future rather than the past. It does not exclude, however, using the past to understand the present and predict what might happen in the future. Whether regression is to be encouraged or discouraged in the treatment of schizophrenia is a controversial issue; the assertion here is that it should be discouraged. The psychotherapy described in this chapter focuses on exploring the nature of the patient's problems and the kinds of stresses that precipitate them, as well as on the psychotherapeutic relationship itself. Exploration of the problems and examination of the psychotherapeutic relationship are seen here not as conflicting approaches but as two aspects of therapy that complement each other.

The kind of psychotherapy used with long-term patients does make a difference. Just putting patient and therapist in a room together for an hour a week does not automatically result in improvement for the patient. Whitehorn and Betz (1975) have shown that the success rate of psychotherapy with schizophrenics depends very much on the therapist's style and techniques. In this research they found that successful therapists grasped the personal meaning and motivation of the patient's behavior and were not content with mere clinical description and narrative biography. Likewise, these therapists frequently selected goals aimed at helping patients to modify their adjustment pattern in a specific manner and use their assets constructively, instead of seeking merely to decrease symptoms or focusing on psychopathology. The therapists with the lowest success rates tended to be passively permissive whereas the successful therapists frequently expressed their opinions about problems being discussed, voiced honest disagreement at times, sometimes challenged the patient's self-deprecatory attitudes, set realistic limits, and generally were more active in the therapy. The successful therapists conveyed to patients a belief that they had a potential for independent action and thus mastery of their environment and themselves.

A more recent study (Gunderson, 1978) focused directly on clinically meaningful personality dimensions of both patients and therapists. This study showed that (1) composed therapists work especially well when matched with schizophrenic patients who are anxious; (2) therapists judged to be comfortable with aggression work well with hostile patients; (3) grandfatherly therapists do well with seductive schizophrenic patients; and (4) therapists considered to be comfortable with depression do well with depressed schizophrenic patients.

This chapter describes psychotherapy in the community, not in the hospital. It has been shown that psychotherapy in hospitals can improve the patient's in-hospital behavior but does not affect posthospital adjustment (Anthony, 1972; Messier and others, 1969). In fact, extensive and intensive psychotherapy in the hospital is likely to prolong the stay and increase costs (May, 1969). This is not to say that there should not be one-to-one contact between therapist and patient in the hospital. Such contact, like that described in Chapter Thirteen in connection with day treatment centers, is essential in helping the patient to modify and resolve the precipitating problems that caused the hospitalization and in working out a comprehensive and appropriate aftercare plan. But psychotherapy, as described here, is best utilized after hospitalization. It is what happens after hospitalization that is crucial in determining whether the patient is able to remain in the community and improve his or her level of functioning (Anthony, 1972; May, 1969; Stein, Test, and Marx, 1975).

The effectiveness and relatively low cost of aftercare programs that center around social therapy and chemotherapy should not blind us to the importance of one-to-one psychotherapy with long-term patients. Individual psychotherapy, particularly if it takes a here-and-now problem-solving approach, can be a potent therapeutic tool for which social therapy in the aftercare setting cannot compensate. It gives the long-term patient the opportunity to develop the ability to better understand what kinds of situations provoke anxiety and to develop healthier ways of dealing with them. The patient–therapist relationship itself affords patients an ego-corrective experience and an opportunity for growth by teaching them to trust and to tolerate closeness and by providing a testing ground where they may learn to express anger without losing control.

Insight Redefined

Insight is not to be neglected as a goal for the long-term patient. However, insight must be defined so that therapist and patient both understand what their objective is. For the patient, insight means that symptoms such as delusions, hallucinations, and feelings of "falling apart" are understandable; the symptoms mean the patient is under stress and reacting to it. Since the symptoms make sense, patients are no longer overwhelmed by mysterious, frightening, all-powerful forces beyond their control. After helping the patient to see this, the therapist works toward the recognition that logical, purposeful actions can follow from such insight. The patient must not panic but must try to understand what stress is producing the anxiety and hence generating the symptoms. Having identified the stress, therapist and patient next need to determine what actions need to be taken to resolve the problem. In the meantime, patients must understand that increasing their medications will alleviate their symptoms and help maintain their problem-solving abilities. Insight is very meaningful in treating long-term patients if the insight is here-and-now and reality-based. That is, patients need to understand what kinds of situations are extremely anxiety-provoking and that there are certain ways to deal with or avoid these situations. Patients also need to consider how they interact with family and friends and how these interactions need to be changed.

Case Example: A 46-year-old married woman had had numerous state hospitalizations for psychotic episodes over the past fifteen years. She had been out of the hospital for two and a half years, and although on fairly high doses of psychoactive medications she continued to have ideas of reference and, at times, paranoid delusions. When especially upset, she was certain that everyone was saying she ate her own feces.

Many of her early weekly sessions with the therapist centered on helping her recognize these ideas of reference and delusions as symptoms—indicators that she was anxious and under pressure. She was at first skeptical, but since she had a positive relationship with her therapist she was willing to entertain the idea. After four or five sessions, she was able to say, "I must tell you that I understand this on an intellectual level, but I'm not sure I really believe it down deep. Since I trust you, I'll operate as if I really believed it." By examining her symptoms each time they occurred, she was able, with the therapist's help, to identify the particular stress that had precipitated them and to formulate a course of action that would resolve the situation. By dealing with her symptoms in this way, she found her life becoming less chaotic and more enjoyable. Further, the situation was not being allowed to deteriorate to a point where the symptoms progressed to fixed paranoid delusions. It was only after six months of this kind of work in therapy that she was able to talk about her delusion of people saying that she ate her feces and get some perspective on the fact that at such times her anxiety was especially severe. She was much relieved by being able to understand that the symptoms were indicators of anxiety instead of experiencing them as frightening feelings that seemed very real, very incomprehensible, and utterly beyond her control.

A therapist seeing the patient begin to decompensate under stress will, of course, take immediate action. Sometimes the therapist can manipulate, or compromise with, the patient's environment to prevent or reverse this decompensation. But it is crucial that the patient be aware of the rationale for the action and participate in it. Eventually the patient can internalize this active process of recognizing and dealing with stressful situations, based on an identification with the therapist.

The Psychotherapeutic Relationship

The frequency and intensity of one-to-one therapy should be adjusted to the patient's tolerance; it can be one hour a week, one hour every other week, half an hour a week, half an hour once a month, or whatever seems appropriate. Except at times of crisis, therapists should be very hesitant to see a schizophrenic patient more than one hour a week because of the danger of developing a transference that neither therapist nor patient can handle. Schizophrenics generally have difficulty handling the closeness and regression that develop in intensive psychotherapy. To ignore this is to invite a transference psychosis (Fox, 1973a).

Case Example: A 32-year-old married woman began outpatient therapy following a psychotic episode that required hospitalization. It soon became clear that she had had a thought disorder and paranoid ideas for a number of years. In the first interview, she became extremely anxious and insisted that her husband be called inside from the waiting room. She was unable to explain what had happened but did ask that her husband be with her in subsequent sessions. The therapist agreed. There were numerous problems in the marriage that needed to be discussed, and the patient seemed willing to talk about other problems in her husband's presence. On one occasion several months later, she arrived before her husband, again became very anxious, and again could give no explanation. From then on she and her husband always came together.

The therapy progressed well. After being seen weekly for several months, every other week for another six months, and monthly for a year, her visits were put on an as-needed basis. It was agreed that either she or her husband would call for an appointment if problems arose they could not handle together. This they did, coming in approximately once a year for a joint session. But about seven years after her first interview, the patient called and requested to come in alone. When she arrived, she reported that although her life and her marriage were going well she had two special reasons for coming. First, she wanted to tell the therapist that initially she had been afraid she would lose control and ask the therapist to have intercourse with her on the couch in the office. Second, she felt that she now had more control and wanted to prove to herself that she could sit in the office with her therapist for an hour and maintain control, which in fact she did. Further discussion revealed that beneath the concern about sexual intimacy was a more basic fear of losing control generally and allowing herself to be dependent and at the mercy of another person in a close relationship. She had used her husband's presence to dilute the relationship with the therapist and, considering the amount of anxiety involved, had probably prevented what might have become a transference psychosis.

There are other techniques that can help keep the patient's anxiety at a manageable level. Long silences should be avoided. Eruptions of unconscious material at a rapid pace should be discouraged.

Treatment of long-term patients is a long-term process. A frequent error is premature termination of therapy. This does not necessarily mean that the patient should be seen for an hour a week indefinitely. But with the long-term schizophrenic there is no real ending (Mendel, 1975). The therapy may be reduced to once a month, or to twice a year, or to times of crisis only. For that matter, there may be lifelong maintenance of the therapeutic relationship. Even if there is only an occasional telephone call or perhaps no contact at all, the memory of the therapy stays with the patient, who knows the therapist is only a telephone call away.

Strengthening Ego Controls

There is a popular notion that if a therapist can help patients to "express their anger," something very therapeutic has been accomplished. And indeed this is often true, especially with non-schizophrenic patients. But with long-term schizophrenics, a sudden explosion of anger may really signify a psychotic loss of control that can lead to a further loosening of controls generally and quite possibly to a hospitalization. The anger may be so intense and the ego control so tenuous that here one should tread with caution. Nevertheless, appropriate expression of anger over which the patient has control can be a major goal of long-term treatment. On a short-term basis, one should be cautious, paying fully as much attention to the patient's ability to retain control as to the underlying anger.

Case Example: A 41-year-old man, a chronic schizophrenic, had been able to function quite well in a minor executive position between his infrequent psychotic episodes. Each episode, however, had been characterized by extreme anger and paranoia. In remission he was a pleasant, friendly man with little overt hostility and universally described as a "nice guy." In therapy, each time the therapist allowed the situation to reach the point where the patient was expressing real anger, the patient began to decompensate. So, during the first few years of therapy, the therapist began encouraging the patient to suppress his anger. Each time the patient reconstituted and continued to function well.

As the relationship progressed and the patient felt more confident that his therapist would support him if he began to lose control, he began to assert himself, at first in small ways and later in more significant ways. It was a slow process, but after four years the patient was able to become overtly angry at his wife and more aggressive at work without losing control, disrupting his marriage, losing his job, or requiring hospitalization. He now has a gratifying sense of mastery over his angry impulses. Certainly his ability to be appropriately aggressive and at times angry without losing control has been healthy for him in terms of his mental health and improved relationships with his wife, employer, coworkers, and others.

A similar snare awaits the unwary therapist who tries to change the character structure of a borderline psychotic who has a saccharine exterior covering a tremendous amount of underlying hostility. In the short term, such a character structure is best left intact as a necessary defense against a psychotic loss of control over angry impulses; in some cases, changes can be effected over a long period of time. But often this character structure is so necessary to help a weak ego deal with an immense amount of anger that little or nothing can be done to change it even over a span of years. Therapists must settle for what is possible. Not every person who walks into the therapist's office can depart a well-analyzed person in tune with all his impulses and a model of mental health. Even though a character defense may annoy the therapist, it is far better than having a patient abandon the defense and then become overtly psychotic.

Another way to help patients develop ego control is by encouraging them to confine their thinking to reality and preventing them from drifting off into ruminations about normally unconscious, primary-process fantasy. Suppose a woman with weak ego strength begins talking about a dream in which she had intercourse with her father. There is a great temptation here to get into a discussion of oedipal feelings, incestuous tendencies, and all the dynamics that flow from such a dream. A fascinating hour? Probably. But that evening or the next day one is quite likely to have to deal with an overtly psychotic patient. One should not ignore such material but rather should help the patient repress it. The therapist can say, "You love and miss your father, and sometimes it shows up in dreams like this. The sexual part of the dream disguises your feelings of closeness for him." If it seems desirable, patient and therapist can then discuss the father in reality terms. Or they can go on to some other pressing issue. As this procedure is repeated in therapy, the patient learns how to turn away from primary-process material and, with ego more intact, feels better equipped to grapple with the problems of life.

The therapist can supplement ego control by setting limits on behavior: Don't stop therapy, continue taking your medication, don't impulsively quit your job. Retaining the therapist's approval is itself often sufficient incentive for the patient to adhere to the therapist's limits. Occasionally the family can become involved in enforcing limits. At the outset, the patient is the passive recipient of limits and passively complies. In successful therapy, however, by identification with the therapist, the limits are internalized— strengthening patients' inner controls and enhancing their ego functioning and their feeling that they can control their own destiny.

Giving Advice

Many long-term patients lack the ability to cope with the routine stresses of life. If these stresses are discussed in individual therapy, patients may be helped to resolve problems they cannot handle alone. Sometimes the procedure is the same as that used with healthy patients: The therapist acts as a catalyst, enabling patients to identify the alternatives and choose the ones right for them. In other cases, the therapist may give direct advice. Giving advice may not come easily to the therapist, but it can be crucial to the success of the therapy. Sometimes the same advice has to be given again and again to patients whenever their maladaptive pattern of reacting to a certain stress is repeated. But one hopes that patients will learn new ways of handling situations and arrive at solutions themselves when the next crisis comes.

Case Example: A 36-year-old married woman had been hospitalized five times for acute psychotic episodes between the ages of twenty and thirty-one. For the past five years she had been doing well in outpatient psychotherapy: no hospitalizations and no overt psychosis. Her therapy, which initially had been once a week, was now once a month.

She was on vacation, visiting her mother in a distant city, when she called the therapist, obviously disturbed and in the incipient stages of a psychotic episode. Unraveling the story over the phone, the therapist finally ascertained that she had been going through her mother's cedar chest bringing out all kinds of mementos from the past. Finally she had come across a birthday card she had received from her now dead father on her eleventh birthday. He had written "Happy birthday to a good little girl who is doing the dishes on her own birthday." She was being flooded with memories of the deprivation she had experienced as a child, the unreasonable demands that had been placed upon her, and the feelings of loss for her dead father, about whom she still felt quite ambivalent.

The therapist's response was "Put all those things back and close that cedar chest." The patient complied. When she called back an hour later, she was much less distraught; she now felt in control of the situation and a psychotic decompensation had been averted. In succeeding visits over the years, she did not reopen the cedar chest either literally or figuratively.

People from lower socioeconomic classes, in particular, expect a professional to give advice, and the therapy may fail if advice is not forthcoming (Carlson and others, 1965). But nothing is more difficult for many therapists than to give direct advice and to give it in simple language without jargon. Nevertheless, the following example illustrates what can be accomplished if the therapist feels free to depart from what is usually described as psychotherapy.

Case Example: A middle-aged, chronic schizophrenic woman had first been seen by the therapist when she was hospitalized for a psychotic depression—her husband, unable to tolerate her hostility, her seclusiveness, and her alliance with her mother against him, had suddenly left her. Driving all the way across the continent, he became increasingly overwhelmed by guilt with each mile. Finally he could stand it no longer and turned the car around and returned. The reconciliation in the hospital was not exactly a joyous one, but the patient went into remission, and following her discharge from the hospital, the marriage continued. The patient refused regular outpatient treatment but has, over the years, called at times of crisis. Each time there has been direct intervention by the therapist, and the patient has not had to be hospitalized.

In a typical example of one of these episodes, the patient, very disturbed and talking about suicide, called the therapist and requested an appointment. She could give no clear picture of the problem over the telephone. The patient arrived for the interview with her husband, a burly, unsophisticated, but long-suffering and well-intentioned truck driver. A half hour of exploring all the known trouble spots in this couple's lives finally revealed the problem. The husband had been waging a campaign for the past year to induce the patient to go out more, spend less time with her mother, and have some social life. Since she had no teeth, he had prevailed upon her to get dentures as a first step in making herself presentable in public. The patient repeated over and over again, "My dentures don't fit, so I'm going to kill myself." Clearly, what she meant was that she did not want to change her life-style, did not want to wear the dentures, and was very angry at her husband for attempting to force her to do so.

The therapist and the couple had been through this issue before. The patient had been urged to spend more time outside the home many times, and it had long since become clear that this seemingly iron-willed woman was not only unwilling but unable to change. The therapist now took a directive stance. To the husband he said, "Joe, I realize that these dentures cost a lot of money and you really resent your wife not wearing them. I also realize that it bothers you that your wife will not go out with you and spends so much time with her mother. But I don't think there's any way to change the situation. If you want things to settle down at home and the kids to be less upset and your wife not to end up in the hospital, I think the best thing for you to do is forget about the dentures and leave it up to your wife whether or not she wears them." The husband groaned, but he seemed to recognize that it was a question of either accepting the situation or leaving again, which he was not psychologically prepared to do. Reluctantly he agreed, and the patient responded, "Fine, then I won't wear them." The therapist said, "No, Roseanne, I don't think you should leave it at that. You should at least go with your husband to his union picnic. It's very embarrassing for him not to show up, year after year, and you owe it to him to attend and make yourself look presentable when you do." She too groaned, but she too agreed. As usual, however, she would not agree to return for further discussion of these issues.

A call from the patient a week later revealed that both parties had abided by their agreement and the situation had returned to its usual unsatisfactory equilibrium. Despite their complaints, both husband and wife seemed able to live with the situation and even to derive some gratification from it. No more was heard from the couple until the next impasse, about eighteen months later. The patient no longer needs to become psychotic to resolve these situations; she knows she can call the therapist for advice and arbitration.

Case Example: A 42-year-old, married, schizophrenic woman had had an intensely ambivalent relationship with her alcoholic mother. Throughout her adolescence and into her adult life, the patient continued to seek from her mother the love and nurturing she had missed as a child; repeatedly the mother disappointed her and the patient experienced over and over her childhood resentment.

When the mother died suddenly, the patient became extremely anxious and guilt-ridden. As her thinking was becoming increasingly disorganized, she was brought immediately to her therapist by her husband. Both patient and husband agreed that she could not attend the funeral—she would become overwhelmed by her feelings and fall apart completely. The therapist, on the other hand, realizing the depth of the patient's guilt, thought it would be intensified if she did not attend the funeral. Further, he felt that the ritual and structure of the Catholic mass and funeral service would help this woman cope with her mourning. He strongly advised the patient to go to the funeral service, but not to the grave site. Reluctantly the patient attended the mass as instructed; afterward, she was much relieved. Though the work of mourning continued for some months, the crisis had passed.

Frequently it is helpful to assist the patient to rationalize a situation and thus save face and self-esteem. Take, for example, a man for whom being in psychiatric treatment means that he is sick, inferior, not really a man. Often these feelings can be dealt with in time, but for the moment the important thing is to keep him in treatment and his illness in remission. The therapist might say, "You know how concerned your wife is about you and how fearful she is you'll have another breakdown. The more worried she gets, the more she upsets you—and the more preoccupied you become with the problems at home, the less you can function at work. So it's really important for you to remain in treatment to allay your wife's anxiety, make her life more comfortable, and in the process make your own life more comfortable." Of course, this should only be said if in fact the wife does have this reaction. Although it is only part of the picture, it is a rationalization that helps patients remain in treatment while retaining the self-image necessary for their psychological well-being.

Or take a person whose vocational potential appears limited but whose vocational aspirations are high. Referral to a sheltered workshop is indicated, but how can one do it without shattering the person's self-image and self-esteem? Again, assisting the person to rationalize the situation may be crucial. The therapist may say, "It's not that you're going there for life. Look at it as a period of transition leading to your ultimate goal." Although the therapist may have some doubt that the person can in fact go on to competitive employment, the person has been helped to rationalize entry into the workshop. If the patient cannot in fact move on, a year later he may be encouraged to feel that the workshop is his regular job, a place where he is needed for the smooth working of the facility and to break in new clients—an assessment of the situation that may or may not be embellished to help him rationalize remaining there. Not really facing reality? How many people really do? And who would not become depressed if they suddenly had to give up all or even most of their rationalizations?

Dealing with Life's Problems

For the therapist, there is no substitute for possessing maturity and an understanding of the very real problems of the life cycle (Lidz, 1968). These are, of course, problems that affect all of us, not just long-term patients. But the long-term patient's lack of ego strength results in an impaired ability to solve problems. Thus,

much of psychotherapy with long-term patients has to do with helping them handle the problems specific to the phase of the life cycle
in which they find themselves. With adolescent patients, for instance, the therapist needs to understand the stresses of adolescence:
the struggle for emancipation from parents, the conflict and ambivalence about becoming independent, the problems of identity formation, the difficulties of choosing a vocation, the task of achieving
an adequate sexual adjustment, and the necessity of preparing for
the responsibilities of an adult, including the roles of spouse and
parent.

Another phase is what Marmor (1968) has called "the crisis of
middle life." Marmor points out that in mid-life such stresses arise
as the physical signs of aging—that is, the loss of hair and skin tone,
the diminution of physical strength and the battle against weight
gain, intimations of one's own mortality, and the deaths of friends
and relatives. During this period, a powerful stress for most people
is recognition that they may never achieve the high goals they once
set for themselves. And all these stresses come at a time when there is
the greatest demand on one's earning capacity to meet the needs of
the family, including school-age children. The therapist must also
understand the problems of reaching maturity, the pressures of grad-
uation and going out into the world, and the feelings of uselessness
and depression when the children are grown and have left home (the
empty nest syndrome).

Although dealing with these kinds of problems may seem
mundane to some therapists, it is central to psychotherapy, at least
with long-term patients who lack the ego strength to cope with these
problems alone.

> *Case Example:* A 29-year-old schizophrenic woman
> had been seen weekly for one and a half years; her life had
> followed a steady downhill course with several hospitaliza-
> tions. She was the mother of four children and had become
> psychotic shortly after the birth of the second child. Finally
> consultation with another psychiatrist suggested that since
> this woman did not possess sufficient ego strength to nurture
> four children, she was being constantly overwhelmed by the
> task. Work with the family resulted in the patient's mother as-
> suming most of the responsibility for the care of the children;

the patient was helped to rationalize giving up her maternal role without suffering a devastating loss of self-esteem. Then, and only then, could outpatient psychotherapy proceed in the direction of helping her to improve her relationship with her husband and others and to explore the possibility of vocational goals. For this woman a job might well be less stressful than the demands of parenthood.

Existential Factors

It is crucial that the therapist help patients deal with what Yalom (1980) calls the four ultimate concerns: death, freedom, isolation, and meaninglessness. The individual's confrontation with each of these facts of life constitutes the content of the existential dynamic conflict. Yalom (pp. 8, 9) goes on to describe these four concerns:

> *Death:* The most obvious, the most easily apprehended ultimate concern is death. We exist now, but one day we shall cease to be. Death will come, and there is no escape from it. It is a terrible truth, and we respond to it with mortal terror. A core existential conflict is the tension between the awareness of the inevitability of death and the wish to continue to be.
> *Freedom:* Another ultimate concern, a far less accessible one, is freedom. Ordinarily we think of freedom as an unequivocally positive concept. Throughout recorded history has not the human being yearned and striven for freedom? Yet freedom viewed from the perspective of ultimate ground is riveted to dread. In its existential sense "freedom" refers to the absence of external structure. Contrary to everyday experience, the human being does not enter (and leave) a well-structured universe that has an inherent design. Rather, the individual is entirely responsible for—that is, is the author of—his or her own world, life design, choices, and actions. "Freedom" in this sense has a terrifying implication: it means that beneath us there is no ground—nothing, a void, an abyss. A key existential dynamic, then, is the clash between our confrontation with groundlessness and our wish for ground and structure.
> *Existential Isolation:* A third ultimate concern is isolation—not interpersonal isolation with its attendant loneliness, or intrapersonal isolation (isolation from parts of oneself), but a fundamental isolation—an isolation both

from creatures and from world—which cuts beneath other isolation. No matter how close each of us becomes to another, there remains a final, unbridgeable gap; each of us enters existence alone and must depart from it alone. The existential conflict is thus the tension between our awareness of our absolute isolation and our wish for contact, for protection, our wish to be part of a larger whole.

Meaninglessness: A fourth ultimate concern or given of existence is meaninglessness. If we must die, if we constitute our own world, if each is ultimately alone in an indifferent universe, then what meaning does life have? Why do we live? How shall we live? If there is no preordained design for us, then each of us must construct our own meanings in life. Yet can a meaning of one's own creation be sturdy enough to bear one's life? This existential dynamic conflict stems from the dilemma of a meaning-seeking creature who is thrown into a universe that has no meaning.

Yalom argues that most therapists are existentially oriented, often unbeknownst to themselves. At least this claim holds true for most therapists who help their patients. While discussion of these issues directly, in these terms, is only appropriate with certain long-term patients, all therapists need to understand these universal concerns.

Working with the Family

The family should be involved in the therapy on a regular basis, or at least as needed, so that the therapist becomes a person on whom the entire family can rely. Moreover, the educational approach to families described in Chapter Eight can be a powerful therapeutic modality as well as a means of avoiding the feelings of exclusion from the treatment and the feelings of resentment that families, in the past, have felt toward mental health professionals. Generally, however, and especially with long-term patients, the therapist should, except at times of crisis, minimize contact with the family either in person or by phone unless the patient is present. When patients are not present, their fantasies about what has happened "behind their backs" run wild. They may think that the therapist and the family are planning to send them to a hospital. They may think that the family is winning over the therapist against them. They may think that the therapist is telling all their secrets to the family, and as a result they may be extremely hesitant about revealing themselves further to the therapist. All these fears may be avoided by telling the family that the therapist will be glad to see them if the patient is present and consents. (This does not mean, of course, that the family should be discouraged from calling the therapist in urgent situations.)

These considerations should be balanced with the need to retain the family's support and cooperation so that they will aid rather than undermine the treatment process. While the therapist's primary concern is with the patient, he must not be, or even be perceived as, "against" the family. Moreover, the family may need help with their feelings of guilt about the patient's illness. And as we saw in Chapter Eight, there is much the therapist can convey to the family that will greatly enhance the therapy.

Another indication for involving the family is when a spouse is ambivalent about continuing the marriage. It is crucial that the issue be resolved one way or the other—so that either there is a new stability at home or patient and therapist know that new plans must be made. For these reasons the therapist may feel that a family interview should be held even though the patient may be reluctant. The situation can be discussed candidly with the patient, who senses the problem anyway. The therapist should elicit the patient's concerns about what might happen. The patient should be told exactly why the therapist wants the interview and what, in fact, will be discussed. Sometimes the patient is fearful of discussing a certain issue with the family present. If the fear is either legitimate or cannot be worked through, and if there is no pressing need to discuss the issue with the family, the therapist can say, "Fine, in that case we'll avoid that subject with your family."

If it is appropriate to see the family at this time, most patients can accept an explanation. For example: "There are many things your family should know about your illness that will help them understand you better and enable them to work with us to reduce problems at home. I think it's important not to alienate them and cause problems for the therapy. Instead I'd like to enlist their support. There are a number of things that may be beneficial for us to explore together and that may well increase the effectiveness of your

treatment. In any event, you'll be there to hear exactly what is said."
Some families attempt to circumvent this policy of seeing the family
with the patient present by engaging the therapist in long telephone
conversations. Therapists should guard against being drawn into a
phone conversation involving issues that should be discussed in a
meeting with the patient present.

Another note of caution should be sounded. Many schools of
thought implicate the patient's family in aggravating and even generating the illness. Thus, mental health professionals often blame
and abuse the family through open hostility or vague innuendo
(Appleton, 1974). Badly treated families in turn retaliate in ways that
are detrimental to the patient. They become less willing to tolerate
the problems he causes, are less agreeable to changing their behavior
toward him, and do not give information that would help the therapist understand him. We also must recognize that being the relative
of a mentally ill person is traumatic and often overwhelming. Usually the family is already guilt-ridden and has a sense of failure for
having "produced a schizophrenic." To win their confidence and
cooperation, mental health professionals must learn to treat families
with sympathy, understanding, and respect.

Pursuing a similar train of thought, Arieti (1974) observes
that schizophrenics tend to attribute to their parents full responsibility for their illness and despair. This is a natural tendency and may
serve a useful function in warding off severe depression. Unfortunately, many psychiatrists have accepted these perceptions as real
insights and accurate accounts of historical events. Arieti believes it
is the therapist's job to help patients get their parents into perspective by pointing out how the patient distorts and exaggerates. "For
instance, a white lie is transformed into the worst mendacity, tact-
lessness into falsity or perversion" (p. 587). The therapist must be
careful, of course, for in some cases the parents have been depicted
accurately. But when patients come to recognize that their parents
have played a role in their psychological difficulties, they usually
exaggerate and distort that role. They are unable to see their own
distortions until the therapist points them out. Further, patients
must be helped to realize that negative traits of parents or other
important people are not necessarily weapons used deliberately to
hurt them; they may simply be personal characteristics rather than

attitudes directed solely toward the patient. Arieti (1975) hopes that in psychotherapy patients will stop blaming others for all their troubles. While recognizing the role others have played in their life, they should assume some responsibility for what has happened to them in the past and especially for the way they will direct their lives in the future.

Taking Sides Against the Superego

Sometimes the best course of action is to attempt to modify the patient's superego, thereby reducing his guilt and the self-destructive behavior it prompts. In other words, the therapist takes sides against the superego. If the patient reacts to certain situations in a self-destructive way because of lifelong inappropriate feelings of guilt, the therapist must not only point this out but say, "That is self-destructive. Don't do it."

Case Example: A 31-year-old woman had received a constant message during her childhood from her parents and siblings that her role in life was to compensate for the failings of her alcoholic mother and take care of her father and brothers. She had been made to feel that any enjoyment of life was wrong; she should instead be devoting herself to the welfare of her family. As an adult, simply taking a pleasant vacation would overwhelm her with guilt and precipitate a psychotic break.

A critical element in the therapy of this schizophrenic woman was to encourage her to stop taking care of her parents and siblings. She had to be assured that taking a vacation, buying a new home, and enjoying intercourse were not evil but in fact important—important not only for her but for the welfare of her husband and children. Not only was this woman helped to increase her enjoyment of life but the intervention has prevented a number of psychotic episodes and hospitalizations. Early in the therapy, for instance, her therapist's statement "It's not wrong to enjoy a vacation" reduced her guilt and helped her to enjoy the vacation without becoming symptomatic. But for her it was an external and unfamiliar way of viewing the situation. As therapy progressed, the reduction in guilt became internalized, her superego became modified, and she became less dependent on the therapist to deal with and master what had been disabling guilt.

This case is not unlike the corrective emotional experience described by Franz Alexander in which the therapeutic benefit derives from the therapist's reacting, in the more favorable circumstances of the transference relationship, in a way very different from the parents' behavior in the patient's earlier life (Alexander, French, Bacon, and others, 1946).

Guilt reduction can be extremely useful in a variety of ways. This point is illustrated by another schizophrenic woman, who felt a tremendous amount of resentment about the way her husband was treating her. She thought she was exaggerating the husband's behavior, however, and that in any case she had no right to feel resentment. Her therapist had known the patient and family for over ten years and was in a good position to assess the situation. His response was "You're not exaggerating the way he is treating you at all. And it's a normal, human response to feel resentment about such treatment. Part of the problem is that your parents made you feel that all angry feelings are wrong. It's normal, it's all right, to feel resentful about this." By pointing out that her resentment was appropriate and by reducing her guilt about the anger she was feeling, the therapist was helping the patient see the realities in her life more objectively and to allow herself to have appropriate feelings about them. The result was a lessening of her depression and her need to use psychotic defenses to deal with feelings of guilt.

A Final Word

These examples illustrate still another crucial point that is too often neglected in community mental health—the importance of understanding the individual psychodynamics of long-term patients. Aftercare programs consisting primarily of medication and social therapy, even when the relationships between patient and staff are good and there is a high level of staff involvement, are often superficial. One can find a happy medium between the formal psychoanalysis of the schizophrenic patient and a program consisting only of medication and social therapy. It is important to understand the psychodynamics of patients' illnesses, have at least a modicum of information about their early life, and above all understand the situations that interact with their internal dynamics in such a way as to cause a psychotic episode, interfere with growth, or deprive them of gratification from life. Mental health professionals must be able to combine the techniques of medication, social therapy, and individual and group psychotherapy based on a practical understanding of psychodynamics. They need not apologize if their work is not psychoanalytical psychotherapy delving into the person's childhood. Nor should they feel apologetic about delving into patients' psychodynamics to deepen their understanding of what causes their illness and unhappiness.

Several other themes have been dominant in this chapter. First of all, patients' symptoms should make sense to them and be understood as their reaction to stress. From this understanding can come practical resolution of their problems. Insofar as possible, this resolution should be a joint process involving both patient and therapist. Eventually patients begin to become masters of their own destiny.

Probably no part of therapy with long-term patients is so important as giving them a sense of mastery (Fenichel, 1946, pp. 13, 460) over their internal drives, their symptoms, and the demands of their environment. From their ability to master and cope with both internal and external demands comes not only a better adaptation to the world in which they have to live but also a sharp rise in their self-esteem, their feelings of self-worth. It is in this context that regression, especially in the form of continued psychotic experiences and ego disintegration, is seen as contraindicated. These experiences undermine their self-confidence and sense of mastery and reinforce their conviction that they will always be at the mercy of all-powerful forces, both internal and external, beyond their control.

This chapter has underlined the importance of flexibility. Therapists must work in the present but be able to delve into the past when necessary. At one session they may serve as a catalyst while the patient does the actual decision making and then in the next hour be equally competent in giving direct advice or setting limits. Therapists need to be able to assess when their task is to strengthen the ego and when they need to take sides against the superego. They need to establish a warm, meaningful relationship without exceeding the patient's tolerance for closeness and intimacy.

In short, if therapists are willing to modify many of the techniques they learned for working with patients with quite different problems, they can accomplish a great deal in psychotherapy with long-term patients.

❧ Eleven ☙

Case Management

For satisfactory adjustment into the community, the long-term patient often needs assistance in dealing with a bureaucracy of agencies and departments (Barter, 1978). Many professionals have urged the development of a new kind of mental health worker—the case manager. The case management system is itself susceptible to becoming an impersonal bureaucracy, however. This chapter takes the position that case management functions are part of the normal duties of a conscientious therapist and, moreover, that only through significant therapeutic involvement does a case manager acquire the in-depth knowledge of individual patients to adequately assess their unique needs and facilitate the processes for meeting them. But before we look for solutions, let us first take a closer look at the problem.

In the community, long-term patients must usually look to a host of local, state, and federal agencies, as well as private organizations, to have their needs met for housing, social and vocational rehabilitation, financial assistance, medical care, psychotherapy, and medication supervision. These services, however, are frequently characterized as fragmented, uncoordinated, competitive, and unresponsive. The chronically mentally ill, with their high vulnerabil-

Note: Parts of this chapter originally appeared in two articles by the author: "Therapist-Case Managers: More Than Brokers of Services," *Hospital and Community Psychiatry*, 1980, *31* (11), 762–764, and "Securing Patients' Rights—Responsibly," *Hospital & Community Psychiatry*, 1981, *32* (6), 393–397.

143

ity to stress and anxiety and their tendency to be passive, frequently have difficulty simply coping with the everyday demands of life. Finding their way through the maze of services potentially available to them can be an almost impossible task.

The need to guide them through such a system is obvious. Simply making a referral to another agency or to a staff member in another section within the same agency, even if discussed with the patient and followed by a letter of referral or a phone call, is often insufficient for getting the patient to actually make contact with the agency, let alone receive its services. When a number of agencies are involved, the problem is greatly compounded. To make matters worse, the reluctance of many community mental health agencies to serve long-term patients is well known (Hogarty, 1971; Lamb, 1976), and these patients frequently feel, and are, unwelcome at these agencies.

Generally it is inefficient for one agency, without the aid of other specialized agencies, to try to provide all the components of the long-term patient's community support system. And with many diverse agencies in many different administrative systems, inevitably there are breakdowns in communication and coordination and lack of clearly defined responsibilities. That the system is so complex and fragmented, however, and that we so sorely need this function of case management, is a sad commentary on the bureaucratic systems that have proliferated in our society. Inefficiency, duplication of services, bureaucrats concerned about defending their turf, unreasonable demands for mountains of paperwork—all these things and more have become synonymous with bureaucracy.

The functions of case management vary with different programs and different authors (Melvile, Kibler, and Haddle, 1977; Test, 1979), but they usually include these tasks:

- *Identification of the Population to Be Served:* Who is in need of case management? The answer is usually based on such criteria as history of two or more failures to link with or remain connected with outpatient mental health services, more than two acute hospitalizations within the past twelve months, psychotic diagnosis, psychopathology that renders the person severely dysfunctional or obviously dangerous (either chronically or episodically), lack of family or social support system, and inability to provide basic needs for food, clothing, and shelter.

- *Assessment:* In this process the case manager determines a patient's existing and potential strengths, weaknesses, and needs.
- *Planning:* With the patient's input, activities and services necessary to achieve designated goals are outlined. The plan is subject to periodic review and serves as an accountability mechanism for service delivery.
- *Linking:* Patients are connected with the appropriate services, which requires conferences, telephone calls, and written communication with various support systems in the community.
- *Monitoring and Advocacy:* Monitoring refers to the continuous evaluation of progress during treatment. The primary guide for the monitoring process is the treatment plan. Advocacy is intervention by the case manager with the various components of the support system on behalf of the patient.
- *Review and Updating:* This process involves reviewing the treatment plan regularly and updating it to reflect the person's changing needs.
- *Resource Development:* The case manager may need to use existing resources more creatively, rather than developing a new service. When a new service or agency is needed, a strong case, backed up by actual clinical experience with the patients, must be made to mental health planners and legislators.

An Integral Part of Therapy

The case management function has been made necessary not only by the special needs of long-term patients but also by the nature of bureaucracy. But this does not mean that case management, too, must be impersonal and bureaucratic. In my view, the case manager should not be simply a broker of services but should have the primary relationship with the patient. While carrying out the functions outlined previously, the case manager should also be the patient's primary therapist and the person who works with the family.

Among the most essential parts of therapy are assessing patients' ego strength and capabilities, discussing their preferences with them, making the referral, and providing ongoing monitoring and liaison. To help the long-term patient establish a satisfactory and satisfying life in the community usually requires a person who provides support and encouragement, has a thorough understanding of the patient, and has earned the patient's trust. For these reasons, those who perform case management functions should be referred to as "therapist/case managers" rather than simply case managers, and should be persons who are well trained.

This view does not mean that the therapist/case manager should be doing in-depth psychotherapy; in many instances it may be contraindicated, as generally the most valuable psychotherapy with long-term patients involves dealing with the realities and day-to-day issues of life and survival in the community. It is nevertheless important to understand the psychodynamics of patients' illnesses, have at least a modicum of information about their early lives, and above all to understand what kinds of real-life situations interact with their internal dynamics to trigger psychotic episodes, interfere with growth, or deprive them of gratification from life. Further, someone needs to know about the significant events in the patient's current life and how the patient is reacting to them. A patient can derive little benefit from vocational rehabilitation if all his energies are involved with a divorce, a separation, the loss of a loved one, or any major change in his life. Nor is a person ready for a step toward independent living if he can barely cope with the increased pressure and responsibilities of a new job.

It is difficult to possess all this knowledge outside the context of a therapeutic relationship. And, further, how can therapy be separated from case management? Does the patient possess sufficient ego strength to engage in competitive or sheltered employment? Is he willing to risk another failure? Should he return to his family, or does he need a placement? What do the patient and family want?

Who is in a better position to answer these questions than the therapist? And what is the rationale for therapists going through an intermediary case manager to make the referral and provide all the needed information rather than making the referral themselves? In the ongoing collaboration among treatment and rehabilitation agencies, innumerable questions arise in regard to such issues as patients' readiness to take another step, their suitability for another service or mode of treatment, and how to manage an unanticipated setback. Dealing with such issues is part and parcel of the therapist/ case manager's role—and he or she can deal with them directly. A broker of services would need to say, "I'll have to call the therapist and get back to you."

Adding an intermediary broker of services is a bureaucratic solution to a service system problem; rather than analyzing the task that needs to be performed and what has gone wrong, one simply adds another layer of services. If it is granted that long-term patients need both therapy and case management, then why not combine these functions? If therapists fail to do case management or do not want to do it, or if therapists (and agencies) do not want to treat long-term patients, or if agencies resist collaborating with each other, why not deal directly with these issues rather than simply add another member to the team? This step only invites another opportunity for breakdown of communication.

Extent of Responsibilities

Obviously it is not making good use of a skilled therapist's time, in most instances, to spend half a day accompanying the patient to the Social Security office or to find housing. Paraprofessionals—community workers, mental health workers, or whatever term is most acceptable—should be on call to therapist/case managers to accompany patients on such trips. If carefully monitored, such a system might resolve many of the problems of the private therapist who does not have time, or the desire, to do case management for severely disabled patients—or avoids such patients altogether.

Patients frequently do not understand the purpose of therapist/case managers and either fail to make their needs known to them or resist their efforts. One of the most important functions of the managers, both initially and on an ongoing basis, is to get the patient to understand how they can be of help.

Should the therapist/case manager become involved with the patient's use of psychoactive medication? If the manager is a psychiatrist, the answer is obviously yes. In the case of a nonpsychiatrist, which is more likely, there can still be important involvement with the use of medication. The manager knows the patient well and is able to recognize the early signals of decompensation or the signs of stress that the patient has not been able to handle in the past.

At this point, a call to the psychiatrist describing the situation often results in an adjustment of the patient's medication. If the manager has been too subtle and the psychiatrist has not been made aware of the need to adjust medication, the manager should feel free to suggest directly that a change is indicated. Nondefensive psychiatrists will listen to such suggestions without feeling their territory is being threatened. The manager should also encourage patients to take their medication and try to determine whether they are complying.

When patients are rehospitalized, frequently all contact with their rehabilitation workers in the community is severed, to the detriment of the patient and also the hospital and community caregivers. Therapist/case managers should make a point of remaining involved with their patients when they are in the hospital.

Advocacy

Advocacy is a key function of the therapist/case manager, but it is a function in which all in mental health should share. Should not those in the mental health system from the director on down, in partnership with the families of patients, be the primary advocates for the mentally ill? If we need "patients' rights advocates" to monitor us, something is either very wrong with us or the system or both.

Advocacy for patients' rights is a concept with a ring to it. When used in connection with long-term psychiatric patients, the phrase conjures up images of helpless people pitted against an impenetrable, impersonal bureaucracy, of people denied both services and civil rights. Implied is the need for a struggle to see that these people are well served and no longer oppressed and victimized. What mental health professionals fail to realize in their haste to embrace the "in" concept of patients' rights is that some militant advocates believe that psychiatric patients are usually grossly mistreated and taken advantage of and that mental health professionals are a power-hungry, insensitive, even sadistic lot.

I do not, of course, refer to the many individuals and groups engaged in *responsible* advocacy to improve services to long-term, severely disabled patients and ensure their civil rights. This kind of advocacy is exemplified by relatives' groups (see Chapter Eight) and by the Mental Health Law Project in Washington, D.C., which has fought forcefully on such issues as the right to treatment and treatment in the least restrictive environment. In my experience, these groups have been extremely sensitive to the needs and welfare of patients.

What, then, is irresponsible advocacy? It is efforts, purportedly on behalf of patients, carried out by "advocates" who do not have sufficient experience with patients to understand their needs and have little appreciation of the harm that can result from misplaced advocacy efforts. As I have illustrated elsewhere (Lamb, 1981), to many such advocates the adversary process itself seems more important than the rights or needs of patients.

Clearly, the increased scrutiny in recent years of the social guardianship role (Roth, 1980), a role assumed by psychiatrists at the behest of society, is all to the good. The parameters of this role, often accepted only reluctantly by psychiatrists, need to be carefully defined, and the possibility of repetition of past abuses needs to be eliminated. There is no question that psychiatric patients are too often underserved and badly served by public agencies and by society generally. They do need advocates to help them improve their lot.

But let us also look at what many extremists in the patients' rights movement are saying. For instance: "Many ex-patients are angry, and our anger stems from the neglect, indifference, dehumanization, and outright brutality we have seen and experienced at the hands of the mental health system. Our distrust of [mental health] professionals is not irrational hostility but the direct result of their treatment of us in the past. We have been belittled, ignored, lied to. We have no reason to trust professionals and many reasons to fear them" (Chamberlin, 1978, p. xiv). Does this description fit you or me? We may not think so, but such statements are probably meant to include us both.

Unfortunately, mental health professionals generally fail to speak out against irresponsible advocacy. Wherever patients' rights activists have pressed, the mental health professions have yielded (Stone, 1979). In the courtrooms and legislatures, even within the mental health system itself, there have seldom been zealous advocates to plead the other side and to present forcefully what professionals feel to be the needs and rights of patients and staff.

Power Without Responsibility

It is seldom realized that the patients' rights activist has power without clinical responsibility. Major problems can result when power is wielded by people who lack an appreciation of the clinical complexities of work with severely ill patients. Patients' rights extremists can enter a treatment facility, talk to patients about the "base motives" of the staff, sow seeds of distrust and disruption, and leave in their wake a group of agitated patients. Too often, little thought is given to the fact that it is the mental health staff who are clinically responsible and left to deal with a group of disturbed psychotic patients, now even more disturbed, with no help at all from the "advocates."

The constructive aspects of advocacy are well described in the literature (Roman and Schmais, 1972; Brooks, 1974, 1979; Stone, 1975; Allen, 1976; Lamb and Oliphant, 1979). But every movement, no matter how well intended, must have its limits. The advocacy movement too must be monitored so that perspective is maintained and there is some assurance that more good than harm is being done. To function as an advocate, one needs thorough training in the characteristics and needs of patients, especially long-term, severely disabled patients for whom advocacy is most appropriate. And what better way is there to know what is appropriate and helpful for these patients, and what is not, than to have acquired competence in the direct treatment of them—and to have experienced personally the problems and unforeseen difficulties of clinical work with them?

Another word of caution is in order. In dealing with other agencies, the role of advocacy generally needs to be carefully thought out. Mental health professionals acting as advocates should be aware that in most cases they should not take an adversary stance right from the outset. Frequently a meeting with representatives of Social Security, welfare, Medicaid, or rehabilitation offices will be effective in solving a problem. Often one finds at these meetings harassed, dissatisfied workers who are as frustrated as the caregivers with the inefficiency and red tape of their agencies. Further, they may explain how to satisfy the regulations and not infrequently reveal how to bypass them; in a bureaucracy, for each and every regulation there is a way to get around it.

Sometimes a more aggressive role *is* needed. Too often, however, the advocacy role becomes like war—a license to ventilate hostility.

A Final Word

Among the chief criticisms of state hospitals has been their impersonal nature and dehumanizing effects. Mental health professionals must be constantly on guard to ensure that, in serving patients in the community, they maintain a system of treatment and rehabilitation that provides warm, human relationships with patients and recognizes them as individuals. To accomplish this aim they should avoid conceiving of the case manager as simply a broker of services and instead accept and employ the concept of the therapist/case manager.

∝ Twelve ∝

Supplemental
Security Income:
Benefits and Problems

Almost two decades have passed since eligibility for Aid to the Disabled (ATD) was extended to the mentally ill. Over seven years have elapsed since this program was transferred to the Social Security Administration and renamed Supplemental Security Income (SSI). Has a social, political, economic, and psychological phenomenon as important as this received the scrutiny it deserves? The extension of eligibility for ATD, now SSI, to the mentally ill in 1963 had a major impact on psychiatry. What have been the benefits and what have been the adverse effects of this eligibility? And what can be done to ensure that the large proportion of the long-term mentally ill who require SSI are initially approved to receive it and then are successful in retaining their eligibility?

Benefits of the Shift from ATD to SSI

The beneficial consequences have been impressive. Above all, a source of funding became available that made it possible for

Note: Parts of this chapter originally appeared in two articles: "Supplemental Security Income and the Sick Role," by H. R. Lamb and A. S. Rogawski, *American Journal of Psychiatry,* 1978, *135,* 1221–1224, and "Obstacles to Psychiatric Rehabilitation," by H. R. Lamb, *Journal of Clinical Psychiatry,* 1981, *42,* 130–131.

the mentally ill who are unable to support themselves through work or private funds to move out of state hospitals and be maintained in the community. Previously, state governments had been willing to bear the cost of state hospitals, making only feeble and scattered attempts to provide funding for community alternatives. Although the frequently adverse consequences of prolonged state hospitalization were evident and made known to the public on occasion through newspaper exposés (Deutsch, 1948), the fear of the mentally ill and the public's apathy and desire to isolate them in locked and usually distant institutions prevailed. The advent of psychoactive medications and the community mental health movement made it feasible for the mentally ill to live outside the massive, impersonal institutions, but only the availability of ATD funds enabled those without resources, who would have been destined to spend their lives in state hospitals, to be placed in a variety of community living arrangements. These settings ranged from good to poor, from independent living to single-room-occupancy hotels. In some cases ATD payments made these patients more acceptable to their own families; before this financial support was made available the patients had sometimes been regarded as an economic and emotional burden. Although there were many indignities to be suffered in the process of being approved for ATD, the end result was a dependable source of income for the mentally ill. I am convinced that thousands of patients could have been discharged from state hospitals years earlier had ATD been available to them. Furthermore, the extension of welfare and income maintenance to the mentally ill meant that their needs were at last recognized; prior to this, ATD was available only for the physically disabled.

From the beginning there were concerns about potential problems with this process—particularly in regard to officially labeling this group "totally disabled" and "mentally ill" and thereby stigmatizing them. Because of this danger, "Aid to the Totally Disabled" was changed to "Aid to the Disabled." The program was, however, still called ATD. To indicate the possibility of recovery, a periodic review of eligibility was required by the regulations although it was usually performed perfunctorily. While these changes were a step in the right direction, the term *disabled* was impressed on the minds of recipients, who generally continued to feel labeled and stigmatized.

The change from ATD to SSI in January 1975, and the shift in administration from welfare departments to the Social Security Administration, has lessened the stigma of ATD for some patients (Liebman, 1976). One study (Lamb and Goertzel, 1977) revealed some of these effects. Most of the subjects in this study referred to themselves as being "on Social Security" or "on Social Security insurance." Their financial support no longer clearly labeled them (in their own eyes at least) as psychiatrically disabled, and most no longer considered themselves to be on welfare. The term Social Security had a more normative sound to recipients. Thus, SSI has resolved, at least partially, some important problems for some of the mentally ill.

But Estroff (1981, p. 169) makes a strong argument that for many others "SSI represents one of the most permanent and visible labels the clients possess. It is the culmination of the chronic client-labeling process." She points out that patients have to reveal their source of income when applying for housing and some are turned down because of this. Moreover, they have to attest under oath on their SSI application forms that they are disabled and must specify this disability as mental disorder. Even in superficial conversations with strangers the patient's lack of a job and means of income are usually revealed.

Secondary Gain in SSI

In recent years, new interest has developed in treatment and rehabilitation programs for long-term, severely ill psychiatric patients. A component of such programs is usually social and vocational rehabilitation designed to enable these patients to join in the mainstream of society and experience the satisfactions of participation and even production.

To what extent does the aspect of secondary gain inherent in SSI interfere with such an approach? Although much has been written about compensation neurosis, little has been said publicly about the corresponding, although more subtle, problems inherent in the SSI program. Perhaps we do not mind paying for mental illness so long as it keeps patients quiet and out of sight. It is the thrust of this chapter that serious consideration should be given to all aspects of the impact of SSI on the psychiatrically disabled. Let us turn first to problems of vocational rehabilitation.

An event in Missouri highlights the disincentive effects of SSI. When ATD was made readily available for psychiatric patients, one third of those enrolled in sheltered workshops precipitously quit (Hilary Sandall, personal communication, May 1976). Unfortunately, no follow-up study was done and we do not know how these patients fared in the long run. This event did make the problem clear, however. We talk of appropriating large sums of money for vocational rehabilitation for the mentally ill, but at the same time we undermine their already weakened resolve to overcome their apprehension and try to deal with the everyday demands of life, such as self-support and achievement of a measure of independence.

Frequently, although by no means always, the severely mentally ill have a reduced work capacity. For many, the routine demands of work and social relations are major stresses. So much effort goes into their struggle with illness that they have little energy left to deal with a work situation. Handling interpersonal relationships with supervisors and coworkers is a major stress. The very thought of work is frightening, for it carries the risk of yet another failure. A therapeutic or at least protective work setting and an adequate preparatory period of vocational rehabilitation should be made available for many of these precariously compensated people.

Those who believe in the value of vocational rehabilitation stress that heightened self-esteem issues from experiencing oneself as productive, making a contribution to society, and achieving at least partial self-support and independence. Work therapy is recognized as being fully as important as talking therapy. Having no reason to get up in the morning and no structured day to look forward to causes profound feelings of emptiness in the lives of most of the severely mentally ill. Rewarding and gratifying use of leisure time is equally important. A combination of work and play is both normative and curative.

How does this square with a system in which continued financial support at a low standard of living is contingent upon the patient maintaining a sick status? When one includes Medicaid, food stamps, the supplement to the basic federal grant supplied by a number of states, the exemption from income taxes, and the possibility of pooling one's resources with another recipient, the standard of living may not be so low. It is not surprising that a large percentage of the mentally ill remain "disabled" and totally (or almost so) dependent on SSI. Most of these persons could be rehabilitated only into low-paying sheltered employment or entry-level jobs at minimum wages even if they succeeded in overcoming their fear that they will lose one of the cornerstones of what little security they have: their SSI status (De Lott, 1976). The secondary gain of illness, already a problem with many long-term psychiatric patients, is thus further reinforced.

> *Case Example:* Mr. A, a 26-year-old man, had been hospitalized three times with a diagnosis of paranoid schizophrenia. His social worker suggested that he apply for SSI during his second hospitalization, and he has now been on SSI for two years. He has held a number of entry-level jobs, but none for more than six months and none in the last two years. He is now seeing a psychiatrist and takes antipsychotic medication regularly. He was referred to a vocational rehabilitation counselor who thought Mr. A could handle a low-pressure job, providing that he remained in treatment. The counselor arranged for him to be interviewed for a job as groundskeeper at a golf course. The foreman there handles his employees well and has supervised ex-mental patients in the past with good results.
>
> The prospect of being a groundskeeper appealed to Mr. A. He liked outdoor work, and the job would involve minimal demands to interact with other people. He found staying home all day difficult and depressing; he did not know how to answer when people asked what he did. Mr. A was interviewed and hired, but later that day he called the boss and quit the job. Why? Later he talked with his counselor about his fear of failure. Despite reassurance from both his counselor and the Social Security office, he could not be convinced that he would not lose his SSI permanently if he accepted the job; he could not forget the red tape and interminable delays involved in getting SSI initially and then again when he was discharged from the hospital and had to be reinstated. Besides, Mr. A told his counselor, his net pay from the job (at minimum wage) would be little more than

his SSI check (which includes the California supplement) plus food stamps. He would be taking quite a chance, and he was frightened. Two years later, nothing had changed. Mr. A refuses to see his vocational counselor and is depressed and immobilized.

The message given to patients by the SSI system is fully as important as the financial remuneration. Essentially they are told "you are sick, disabled, and unable to work." Rehabilitation may be mentioned, but the patient is seldom convinced. Thus the SSI system does not counteract the pull toward regression and dependency. Its purpose is income maintenance, not helping the person act or feel like a contributing or significant member of society. In terms of their source of income, patients perceive that society expects little of them. If recipients of SSI choose to do so, they have the means to live an undemanding life with family or in a board-and-care home. There is little incentive to participate in a treatment program, either social or vocational. For a significant proportion of schizophrenic patients who have ego strength sufficient only to cope with modest demands and minimal social stimulation (Wing, 1977), this arrangement may be entirely appropriate. Nevertheless, such a system undermines the already reduced motivation of many mental patients, both schizophrenic and nonschizophrenic, who could benefit from rehabilitation programs.

Funding Vocational Rehabilitation

We are in an era of growing unpopularity of expansion or even retention of social programs. Whatever rehabilitation funding agencies may say, and even feel, about the desirability of vocational rehabilitation or work activity programs that improve the quality of life without necessarily leading to paid employment, they must face certain realities. When one is justifying a budget to Congress or to a legislature, for instance, no argument is more persuasive than the potential of a program to rapidly place people in competitive employment—to "transform tax eaters into taxpayers." Such "rehabilitation" programs may seek patients who need little assistance to join the ranks of the employed.

Thus, there is a disinclination to provide the kind of rehabilitation appropriate to the needs of long-term, severely disabled patients. And this holds true not just for services to improve the quality of life but also programs that in the long run are capable of placing individuals in sheltered employment and preparing them for entry-level jobs. These services may take years and are not cheap; funding sources often give lip service to them, but when the final budget is made known, these services are funded in token amounts if they are funded at all. There is, then, a reluctance to provide adequate rehabilitation to the seriously disabled even if they are potentially capable of achieving increased independence through employment. Given the reluctance to fund rehabilitation appropriate to the needs of the severely disabled and the disincentives associated with income maintenance programs, one might conclude, as some in government are starting to imply, that society has decided to "pay off" the mentally ill rather than rehabilitate them.

What Can Be Done?

Steps should be taken to improve income maintenance programs such as SSI. The first step would be to screen individuals carefully for entry into the SSI system and encourage them to apply only if they are truly disabled. A major problem is the pressure from local jurisdictions such as cities and counties to divert persons from general relief or general assistance (funded entirely by local money) to SSI (funded primarily by federal and state money). Since SSI usually provides more money than general relief, sometimes the pressure comes from a patient's case manager or therapist.

Mental health professionals often contribute to the problem; we are frequently reluctant to see our patients take "low status" minimum-wage jobs even though this is the present limit of their capabilities. Middle-class professionals need to guard against a tendency to view nonprofessional or nonintellectual work in terms of their own subjective reaction to it (Mackota, 1976). Concentrating on the aspects of work they themselves find dull, monotonous, and even degrading, they often fail to see that others can achieve as great a sense of mastery and self-worth by success in whatever job is within their capabilities as professionals do in theirs.

Individuals who need general relief only for a temporary crisis may find themselves propelled into a system where, despite the required yearly SSI review, they may remain for years or even life. At times in the past the mere fact that a person was in psychotherapy seemed sufficient to a welfare department eligibility worker to initiate an SSI application, even though the person may have functioned well in the recent past and was only temporarily disabled. Such inappropriate entries into the SSI system need to be reevaluated; primary consideration should be given to the patient's *long-range* interests.

Another way to reduce the occurrence of chronic regression in the SSI system is to make yearly SSI reevaluations more meaningful. Currently they consist of a financial eligibility check that is essentially mechanical; there is little concern for the patient's other needs. Instead, each patient should be carefully and sensitively evaluated by rehabilitation professionals who would offer the opportunity of social and vocational rehabilitation suited to the individual patient. Patients who are not likely to withstand the stress of such activities should not be pressured or made to feel guilty about not participating in them. Further, the opportunity to receive rehabilitation should be seen both by the patient and the Social Security Administration as a benefit, like Medicaid, not as a requirement. The patient's participation—or nonparticipation—in rehabilitation programs should in no way affect his or her eligibility for SSI.

To minimize the disincentive effects of SSI and the sick role, the law now allows SSI recipients to keep a share of earnings from employment. This provision should not only be retained, but great care should be taken to ensure that recipients do not find their checks stopped rather than simply decreased. By the same token there should be prompt restoration of SSI if the patient's effort to work is not successful. Fears of long delays in restoration of benefits deter many patients from even attempting to venture into the world of work.

Since it cannot be predicted which patients will benefit from a social integration program and which might react adversely, every person at the point of application and approval of SSI should be given every opportunity to participate in a comprehensive treatment and rehabilitation program. Whatever services are indicated should be made available: individual and group psychotherapy, social and vocational rehabilitation, training, sheltered work settings, employment assistance, day treatment, linkage to therapeutic housing programs, and social services. Patients should be monitored to ascertain how they respond to treatment and to inducements to greater social and occupational participation. If patients react adversely, manifest an exacerbation of symptoms, or seem refractory to active help, the professional should be able to reset their goals at any point in the process and accept the patients' limitations and possibly their need for a passive, dependent life-style that will make minimal demands on them. But, professionals should leave the door open to treatment and rehabilitation opportunities in the future. In the meantime, they should offer patients services they can or will accept, including the option to call at times of crisis or great stress. Efforts must also be made to upgrade residential facilities and bring treatment and supportive services to patients who are not ready to come to them.

Mental health professionals also have an important role to play with that large proportion of the long-term mentally ill who require SSI. After helping them gain initial approval, the professional can help them retain their eligibility. The two main principles for professionals to remember in this regard are persistence and documentation of disability (Anderson, 1982). Most mentally disabled persons need considerable assistance in finding their way through the SSI application procedure and are especially prone to drop their claims after the first denial. It is at this point, as well as at the time of initial application, that the advocacy of mental health professionals on behalf of their patients is crucial. It should be remembered that there is considerable disagreement even among psychiatrists doing disability determinations on SSI claims and, moreover, that a large proportion of denials are reversed by administrative law judges upon appeal (Anderson, 1982).

A Final Word

I urge reassessment of a social policy that was conceived in a humanitarian spirit but has brought about unintended and undesirable results. The topic is often avoided by professionals who fear that even the raising of questions will support the arguments of those who would abolish social programs because they consider any social dependency immoral, even that brought on by psychiatric disability.

⌘ Thirteen ⌘

Day Treatment Centers

Where should the long-term patient turn for help at a time of crisis? In many cases, the patient can find it at a day treatment center and does not have to turn to a hospital. Should there be two kinds of day treatment center—one for acute patients (often called a "day hospital") and another for rehabilitation and maintenance of the long-term patient? My view is that there should be only one kind of day treatment center: one that provides crisis intervention for persons experiencing acute psychoses and severe depressions. As described later in this chapter and in Chapter Fourteen, maintenance of the chronically ill can be achieved as well in other settings with the added advantages of more contact with regular members of the community, such as volunteers and teachers, and more efficient use of mental health professionals. This chapter focuses on the issues that bear on the center's functions as an essential resource for the long-term patient.

It is all too easy to take long-term patients and rehospitalize them when they are in crisis and become symptomatic. But many of these patients can be helped through a crisis in a day treatment center rather than in a twenty-four-hour hospital (Lamb, 1967; Herz and others, 1971; Erickson and Backus, 1973; La Commare, 1975; Neffinger, 1980). Since the purpose of a day treatment center

Note: This chapter combines material, revised for this book, that appeared in H. R. Lamb, D. Heath, and J. J. Downing (Eds.), *Handbook of Community Mental Health Practice: The San Mateo Experience* (San Francisco: Jossey-Bass, 1969), and H. R. Lamb and Associates, *Community Survival for Long-Term Patients* (San Francisco: Jossey-Bass, 1976).

should be to deal with acute, short-term problems, persons with a history of many years of mental illness are often not thought of as candidates for such an "acute" treatment center. If one thinks in terms of an acute episode superimposed on a chronic psychotic process, however, the day treatment center clearly becomes suitable for many long-term patients. In this case, the purpose of the day treatment center is not to resolve the chronic, long-standing problem but to get the patient over an acute crisis or to shorten or prevent a hospitalization. In some instances, the center's purpose may be to mobilize and evaluate long-term patients and prepare them for a rehabilitation program.

The day treatment center, then, should serve four types of patients: those in crisis for whom the center will prevent a hospitalization; those in a hospital who can be discharged early only if there is an all-day community program where they can continue their treatment for a brief period before entering an outpatient program; those who are not yet in need of hospitalization but are at risk of admission without a day treatment center; long-term patients in the community who have regressed and need an assessment and rehabilitation plan to bring them back into the mainstream of the community.

If the day treatment center is really serving as an alternative to hospitalization, it will contain many long-term patients, each with an acute crisis superimposed. Why? Because most people with even moderate ego strength can weather the crises of life alone or with some aid from family, friends, or therapists. They do not need a full-time intensive program like a hospital or day treatment center. Of course, there are many people who, under stress, develop an acute depression or psychotic episode and, after a period in a hospital or its alternative, a day treatment center, can return to their usual high level of functioning. But, generally, when a day treatment center is used for crisis intervention, we are dealing with persons with low ego strength— to a large extent the severely and chronically ill.

For that matter, the difference between acute and chronic patients at the point of admission—in terms of appearance and prior functioning—is not so great as has often been thought (Serban and Gidynski, 1975). It has been shown that first-admitted (acute) schizophrenics and their counterpart, chronic patients, do not differ substantially on admission in terms of precipitating crisis events and mental status. Further, first-admission patients show clear-cut impairments in social and vocational functioning for a considerably longer period of time prior to their first admission than the report of sudden onset would indicate. For many, there is evidence of inter-personal and work-associated difficulties dating back to youth and adolescence (Serban and Woloshin, 1974).

The day treatment center also can serve as the hub of a net-work of services for long-term patients. The staff, by helping long-term patients through the time of greatest need—acute crisis—can use the relationship and trust thus developed to involve them in a community network of ongoing rehabilitation and support. This potential is described in more detail later.

If a day treatment center is truly to be an alternative to hospi-talization, staff members must be convinced that providing such an alternative is both possible and desirable. They must also have strong administrative leadership and support. All must feel comfortable with having the acutely psychotic patient in the relatively unstruc-tured setting of the day treatment center. On the other hand, too much administrative pressure can be put on staff to accept *all* acute psychotic patients, even those who are too belligerent, too overac-tive, too much in need of asylum and the structure of a hospital to be manageable in a day treatment center. If it is recognized as a clinical fact that the day treatment center cannot help everyone, patients can be transferred to an inpatient service with a minimum of feel-ings of guilt and failure. Then the day treatment center staff will be less hesitant to accept patients with acute psychiatric problems—secure in the knowledge that they will not have to struggle with those who prove inappropriate for this setting. Some may need only an occasional overnight or weekend stay on a hospital ward during crisis periods while the day center retains primary responsibility for the patient's treatment; other patients may need an intermediate or long period of hospitalization.

Likewise, the staff should not feel that every psychotic patient has to be admitted, no matter how aggressive and out of control he or she may be. For many such patients, an initial, brief period of inpatient treatment, followed by a referral to the day treatment cen-ter when the situation becomes manageable, is a more practical plan

(Lamb and Odenheimer, 1969). Hospital control during this initial period helps the patient go into remission sooner, and the day center staff is not taxed beyond endurance. If pushed beyond its limits, the staff becomes increasingly resistant to treating any acutely psychotic patients. And then admission criteria, wittingly or unwittingly, become ever more selective; the population served becomes very different from that found at an inpatient service (Hogarty and others, 1968); and before long the difficult-to-manage patient is no longer found in the day treatment center.

Clearly Defined Goals

What kind of treatment center are we talking about? It is important to establish a philosophy of what the day treatment center should be, so that staff members have clear objectives. The center must above all be goal-oriented. At every step of the way, the staff must ask themselves and the patient what goals they are striving toward. If the initial goal is to get the patient into remission, and this objective has been accomplished, then what goals are next? If patients no longer need the day treatment center and are ready once more to take their place in society, then they should do so. If they are unable or unwilling to strive toward further day treatment goals, they should move on to other programs, such as outpatient psychotherapy, medication, and social clubs.

Many day treatment centers are used for simple maintenance over long periods of time (Cross, Hassall, and Gath, 1972). In many instances, a mental health program has two kinds of day treatment center: one for acute patients and the other for chronic patients (Beigel and Feder, 1970). In one large system the two types of day programs are described as "day hospitals," whose goal is to treat acute patients so they can return to productive life in the community, and "day treatment centers," whose goal is to maintain and rehabilitate chronic patients (Ognyanov and Cowen, 1974). Dual programs like this are a mistake. They result in day treatment centers that take many people who probably would not be hospitalized anyway and serve basically as an enrichment of outpatient treatment. The day center may, for example, be serving people with personality disorders. These people usually show serious self-destructive tendencies, but they are charming, likable, intellectual, often seductive. Their early lives show much deprivation—so much that endless amounts of staff affection cannot fill the childhood abyss. They do not change, but they do reward the staff. They make endless progress . . . to nowhere. Or the center may become a full-time Monday-through-Friday maintenance facility dealing with chronic schizophrenics for many years. Such service fosters undue dependency and regression and, however well rationalized by patients and staff, should not be the goal of the day treatment center. As we will see in Chapter Fourteen, other programs—such as social rehabilitation clubs staffed by volunteers who receive professional consultation, along with half day a week aftercare programs like the one described later in this chapter—can provide comparable or even superior maintenance services for long-term patients.

By admitting acutely ill patients and clarifying that the center's primary purpose is crisis intervention and the resolution of short-term problems, the staff defines the nature of the center. It is difficult to become a baby-sitting service for chronic schizophrenics or a long-term facility designed to effect personality change in people with character disorders when there is a steady influx of patients in crisis whose needs must be met.

If the patient is over the acute crisis and is interested in rehabilitation, then assessment and formulation of a rehabilitation program is a legitimate goal. But the entire rehabilitation program should not be carried on in the day treatment center. One cannot master one's environment in a setting that encourages prolonged passive dependency. The patient receives a mixed message that makes rehabilitation all but impossible.

The day treatment center should provide only time-limited periods of care (Althoff, 1980). If the patient comes to the center for more than two months, the staff must take a hard look at whether they still have specific goals or are simply gratifying dependency needs. Are they reinforcing patients' sick roles rather than helping them see themselves as persons with strengths and self-worth? "What are the goals for this patient?" is a question worth asking every day.

One should think of limited goals that can be accomplished in the short time available. If patients are taken into a day treatment center with the goal of resolving their core problems ("curing" their schizophrenia or effecting some radical change in their character), one is expecting too much in this setting. Frequently the net result of overambitious therapy is the passage of a year, or sometimes two, without much progress so far as the core problems are concerned. Moreover, a great deal of dependency has been fostered in a setting where long-term care is not only unnecessary but inappropriate. Chronic schizophrenics are particularly susceptible to this problem; many patients who are prone to institutionalism may develop excessive dependence on any other way of life outside a hospital that does not help them realize their potential to be independent (Brown and others, 1966, pp. 205–207).

One does well, therefore, to think in terms of limited goals, for by limiting goals one can accomplish a great deal more in the long run. Although one may not have effected any basic change in the patient's personality structure, such a goal becomes irrelevant if the patient has been restored to a productive, satisfying life in the community. Longer-range objectives can then be attempted in outpatient psychotherapy (see Chapter Ten).

It is important to clarify one's understanding of treatment so that short-term, limited goals can be differentiated from long-term, more far-reaching ones. If staff give themselves two months within which to work, then, no matter how intensive the program, there is only so much that can be accomplished. Getting patients into remission is a reasonable short-term goal; changing their basic personality is not. Assessing the patient and formulating a rehabilitation plan is a reasonable short-term goal; accomplishing the entire rehabilitation plan in the day treatment center is not. Assessing the family situation is an appropriate short-term goal. So is helping family members accept the patient's treatment and recognizing their need to be involved (or uninvolved) by resolving such issues as the family's and the patient's need to spend more time (or less time) with each other; in addition, it is important to help family members become more aware of each other's needs or, alternatively, help them decide to live apart. But effecting sweeping changes in the psychodynamics of a family is better regarded as a goal for therapy *after* the day treatment center.

Distinguishing between long-term and short-term goals is not difficult, so it would seem, but failure to make this distinction has been the rock upon which countless day centers have foundered—mainly because the staff has not had a clear picture of the center's purpose. Patients can be accepted on a trial or evaluation basis of, for example, one month. The patient needs to understand, though, that the period of treatment will be limited and it is essential to formulate goals. Too often, both patient and family are consciously or unconsciously looking for a permanent haven from the pressures of the world—and perhaps from each other; they want to see any institution, including the day hospital, as such a haven. All concerned must be reminded that the day treatment center is a place for actively working out immediate problems, not a place to provide perpetual care.

Psychodynamics of the Here and Now

The day treatment center, and indeed the whole network of rehabilitation services, should have a psychodynamic orientation. In the day treatment center this orientation should involve the dynamics of the here and now rather than those of early childhood. The pertinent questions are, for example, How much ego strength does the patient have? To what kind of pressures is the patient especially susceptible? What current and recent stresses have caused the patient to show symptoms and be in crisis now? (Detre and Jarecki, 1971, p. 132). What has gone wrong in the patient's work or relationships with others? Has the patient sustained a major loss or been under unusual pressure?

As the following case shows, one can easily become preoccupied with the patient's psychopathology or the subtleties of the diagnosis, often at the expense of looking at pressing reality problems and helping the patient deal with and adjust to the rigors of life.

Case Example: A 51-year-old divorced osteopath had spent the last several years in a number of different hospitals. He told a very plausible and interesting tale of dealings with Cosa Nostra, described setting up an impressive osteopathic practice, and gave a detailed narrative concerning intrigue with local and state government. This man was convincing and articulate, and some mental health professionals responsible for the case spent hours debating whether his stories were true or delusional. For others, the question was one of diagnosis. Was this paranoid schizophrenia or bipolar major affective disorder? At each hospital there was case conference after case conference with no resolution; ultimately the patient went to a different city and again was hospitalized. Finally, at the third hospital, the psychiatrists reached a stalemate. The patient had become president of the patient government; he was running the ward and running it well. The staff, meanwhile, was still debating whether he was mentally ill and still arguing about his diagnosis.

The resolution of this impasse was to refer him to a day treatment center for "further evaluation." There the staff focused directly on the realities of the patient's life. A home visit quickly revealed that the sumptuous living quarters he described were in reality an old, unused room of an acquaintance's run-down house. A decision was made to place him on large doses of medication, and the talk of Cosa Nostra soon stopped. An evaluation by a vocational counselor indicated that the patient was not at that point able to handle the pressures of working as an osteopathic physician. It also became apparent that he did not have sufficient funds to set up a practice. Once it was decided that he should lower his goals, the patient quickly accepted the idea of taking an "interim" job as a salesman. He also agreed to remain in therapy and take medication.

This approach may seem obvious, but for those caught up in this patient's psychopathology and diagnosis, it was far from obvious. For the patient, it meant the difference between becoming entrenched in the role of patient and taking his place in the community at a level he could handle, with the support that he needed and with a feeling he could again cope with the real world.

A Comprehensive Program

Still another temptation must be guarded against. Some day treatment centers are open only half a day, offer primarily individual and group therapy with an emphasis on aggressive confrontation, and scorn the activity therapies. This may be an effective program for some, but most of the acutely ill schizophrenics who would otherwise go to the hospital still go to the hospital. It is important to avoid setting up the day treatment center in a way that excludes acutely psychotic patients.

If the center is substituting for a hospital and not just enriching outpatient treatment, a full day is needed. Full-day service gives the patient added support, but it does not mean filling in the day with irrelevant activities. On the contrary, it means recognizing the therapeutic effects of well-planned activities, each with a well-thought-out rationale. The activities should impart to the patient skills that can be translated into his or her life beyond the day treatment center and in the community (Carmichael, 1964). The rationale for each activity should be understood by both staff and patients. A meaningful answer should be forthcoming when someone asks, "Why are you engaging in this particular activity?" Outings show patients how to utilize community resources. Recreation, both indoor and outdoor, helps them learn to use their leisure time and to socialize and enjoy interpersonal relationships. Activity-planning sessions help patients learn how to organize their time in a meaningful way both inside and outside the day treatment center. Role-playing sessions show them how to handle such situations as applying for a job, how to deal with disagreements with a roommate, and how to conduct themselves in various social situations. By emphasizing translatable skills, the program leads to the ultimate goals of productivity rather than dependency, activity rather than passivity, and an early return to the community.

Such activities can be extremely valuable in other ways too. Although therapeutic and educational, they are less anxiety-producing than active group therapy. The activity therapies thus permit patients to spend more time in the center without expending all their energies isolating themselves or otherwise avoiding the intensive interaction and anxiety they would encounter in a program top-heavy with group therapy.

The importance of the activity program should not obscure the fact that it is but one part, albeit a vital part, of a total program. Acute day treatment centers that rely only on a therapeutic milieu, an activity program, and medications are incomplete. Staff members must work with each individual patient to determine what the specific problems are. Once the problems have been identified, staff and patient together are in a position to set goals and resolve these problems. However warm, accepting, and supportive the milieu may be, it does not relieve the staff of the responsibility for taking an individualized, problem-solving approach with each patient.

It is also essential to have a close working relationship with a vocational agency that has a full range of vocational services—including evaluation, testing, counseling, job placement, and a vocational workshop. This arrangement augments the center's effectiveness. It permits staff to deal with a crucial area in the patient's life—the world of work—while he or she is still coming to the center. For patients who will need a vocational workshop after treatment at the center, it leads to a smooth transition from center to workshop. Anything pertaining to work may be frightening for the patient. But while still having the support of the day treatment center, patients can begin the vocational workshop on a part-time basis, perhaps only several afternoons a week. As they become less frightened and more confident, they can gradually increase their time in the workshop while reducing their time in the day treatment center until they spend all their time in the workshop and have been discharged from the center. Sometimes—especially when day treatment centers are used for long-term, simple maintenance—there is no close working relationship with a vocational agency. Instead there is competition for patients, as if the day treatment center needs to prove it is more therapeutic or fears it will lose all its patients to the vocational workshop and be forced to close down. It takes a strong and enlightened administration to maintain an overall program based on need rather than on territoriality and empire building.

Psychoactive Medications

I have spoken of the day treatment center as a facility that can serve acutely ill psychiatric patients. By its very nature, however, the center has less structure than an inpatient service. There probably will be many doors and windows, in contrast to even an open ward, where there are perhaps one or two easily monitored doors through which patients can come and go. Patients remain at an inpatient service twenty-four hours a day and do not have the daily stress of going home to what may be a trying family situation, or living alone where there is little support or contact with people. Day treatment centers are not usually set up so that sufficient staff can be quickly summoned to subdue a patient who has lost control. Since structure is an essential ingredient in the management of the acutely ill patient, the day treatment center must compensate for these lacks in some way. One of the main compensations is a philosophy of treatment that allows the staff to use adequate doses of psychoactive medications.

Hold off giving medication so we can be sure of the diagnosis? By the time we are satisfied with our diagnosis, we may have a patient who needs to be hospitalized. Hold off giving medication so the patient's real problems emerge and can be dealt with? Again, we will frequently find ourselves dealing with the patient's "real problems" in the hospital. To provide ego support and compensate for the center's lack of structure, sometimes more medication is required in a day treatment center than at an inpatient service—especially in the early stages of treatment.

Medication must be given when needed. Since it may be needed when the patient is first admitted to the day treatment center or when staff must respond quickly to head off or deal with a crisis, a psychiatrist must be readily available. The psychiatrist need not work full time in the day treatment center, but he or she must be reachable and able to quickly return at all times when patients are attending the center. If we are to deal with acutely ill patients in this setting, having a psychiatrist come in once or twice a day to prescribe medications or be in the center half the time and be unavailable the rest of the time is not acceptable.

Involving the Family

Probably in no other mental health setting is the involvement of the family so important. Patients go home each night and weekend to their families. Rather than taking the easy way out and simply placing the patient in the hospital to obtain at least temporary respite from the stress of living with an acutely disturbed relative, the family is continuing to provide support and has been asked to participate in the treatment process. The family needs ready access to professionals who can answer their questions, acknowledge that the family itself is under stress, and help them deal therapeutically with problems. Without the support and involvement of the family, treatment in the day treatment center usually fails.

A family diagnostic interview is an important part of the evaluation of every patient in the day treatment center. Initially the family may be seen separately by a staff member other than the person designated as the patient's therapist. If instead, or, in addition, the therapist wants to see the family, the patient and the family should be seen together. As noted in Chapter Ten, the family should not be seen by the patient's therapist unless the patient is present (except at times of crisis).

The family diagnostic interview in which family and patient are seen together gives the staff a unique insight into what goes on between them. The patient might be totally unaware of and unable to describe some of this interaction, but observation helps the staff gauge the accuracy of the patient's perceptions of what his family is like and how he interacts with them. If the staff has the time and the family is willing, every family should be seen on an ongoing basis after the diagnostic interview. Further interviews bring further insights into family dynamics, and the family is able to gain additional support that may be sorely needed during trying parts of the patient's illness. Often, even during the short time the patient is in the center, both patient and family can begin to see their relationship more objectively, make changes, and consider ongoing family therapy when the patient leaves the center.

Many times the family or the patient or both are strongly opposed to ongoing interviews. The family may believe that they are already doing enough, or they may fear such therapy, thinking they will be blamed for the patient's illness. The patient may object out of suspiciousness. If the family or the patient is adamantly unwilling to participate, their decision should be respected. Attempts to involve family members can be made later when they feel less threatened. In any event, the day center staff should learn what the family is able or willing to tolerate and should not get into a power struggle with the family over this issue. Such a struggle may undermine the treatment or even result in the family withdrawing the patient from the center.

Defining Roles

Nothing can be more divisive in a day treatment center than a situation in which certain "high status" professionals have the "high status" tasks—particularly individual and group therapy. This problem need not arise if all members of the staff— psychiatrists, nurses, psychologists, social workers, occupational and recreational therapists, psychiatric technicians, para- professionals—are given the opportunity to participate in and lead group therapy; depending on their other therapeutic commitments, they may also function as individual therapists. If the staff operates as a team and each case is discussed at staff meetings, there is ample opportunity for peer review of what each staff member is doing with his or her patients. If the professional is competent, regardless of discipline, the therapeutic process will in most cases go well— providing that everyone feels free to discuss cases openly at staff meetings and accepts feedback. The staff then feels more like a team, and a minimum of energy is expended in interdisciplinary strife and jealousy. The blurring of roles in this case does not mean that they need not be sharply defined in other areas, however. The psychiatrist has expertise in medication and diagnosis, and usually more exten- sive training; he frequently will be called in as a consultant for difficult cases. Likewise, the social worker, psychologist, psychiatric nurse, occupational therapist, and recreational therapist should be called on as consultants in their particular areas of expertise.

Each staff member should also participate in leading the ac- tivity therapies as time and other responsibilities permit. Here again, there is both a blurring and a definition of roles. All staff members should have some responsibility with regard to the various social rehabilitation and recreation parts of the program, but the occupational therapist and the recreational therapist should be rec- ognized as having particular expertise in these areas and as the per- sons to whom the rest of the staff should turn for leadership and consultation.

Individual Psychotherapy

What is the role of the one-to-one relationship in the day treatment center, a facility that lends itself so well to a team approach and the use of group therapy? Staff members may be tempted to deal with most or all issues in groups and think that individual psychotherapy detracts from the group process. Although many issues are in fact best dealt with using group processes and feedback from the patient's peers (Gootnick, 1971), many issues can be handled more effectively in a one-to-one situation than in a group—especially problems concerning sexuality or the commission of past crimes, which the patient is unlikely to discuss freely unless there is privacy and confidentiality. Suppose, moreover, that a therapist is tactfully trying to help a patient lower his goals without lowering his self-esteem. In such an instance, it may be necessary to help the patient rationalize his inadequacy to handle a certain work or social situation. A one-to-one interaction between a skillful therapist and the patient lends itself much more readily to this process than does a group setting where, in the interests of candor, the patient is encouraged by the group to face the situation "like it is." In the group, the patient may be shattered or may react by summoning his defenses and raising his goals rather than lowering them.

There are, however, special problems regarding individual psychotherapy in a day treatment center. The relationship may become so important to the patient (and therapist) that they become a twosome separated from the group milieu of the center. Further, the patient's time at the center is limited; if one uses *outpatient* intensive psychotherapy as a model, in most cases one has barely reached the opening phase of such treatment by the time it is appropriate to discharge the patient from the center. At this point, one must keep patients longer, which fosters dependency, or patients feel cheated and angry because they have been seduced into opening up painful concerns that are then left unresolved. Moreover, patients may now be more confused and conflicted than before. These pitfalls can be avoided by confining the individual therapist–patient relationship to issues that can be resolved in the time allowed—the precipitating stresses that caused the patient to need the center, the resolution of these stresses, the patient's feelings about giving up a life of dependency and attempting again to compete in the world, and interpersonal problems in the day center that may typify the patient's problems with people generally.

Another problem that frequently arises with individual therapy is the establishment of too close a relationship between the therapist and the patient—especially when this relationship cannot be continued in aftercare. Thus, at the time of separation from the day center, which is at best painful, patients find themselves further burdened by having to give up a very meaningful and important relationship. The shift to another therapist for aftercare as an outpatient is then more difficult and again the patient feels anger and resentment. Equally important is the diversion of the patient's attention from one of the primary goals of day center treatment—namely, resolution of the precipitating problems and a return to functioning in the community.

In one-to-one psychotherapy, the therapist should try to maintain sufficient rapport with the patient to allow the treatment objectives to be achieved, but not so much rapport that the relationship makes separation impossibly painful. The therapist can limit the time spent in individual sessions to a half hour instead of the traditional psychotherapeutic hour, thus reducing transference and lessening the intensity of the relationship. Toward the same end, sessions can be limited to one or two meetings per week, except in emergencies, and should conflict as little as possible with the other activities of the center.

Relationship with the Hospital

A close working relationship with an inpatient service is necessary if the day treatment center is to provide an alternative to hospitalization. This relationship allows the center's staff to attempt to manage more acutely ill patients with the knowledge that they can readily be transferred to inpatient status if they prove unmanageable in the day treatment center. For many patients there will be times of crisis during treatment in the center that require a brief period of hospitalization. Knowledge that hospitalization can be accomplished with a minimum of administrative problems and without permanently giving up the case gives the staff an added feeling of confidence in dealing with acutely and severely ill patients. The patient may stay at the inpatient service for a weekend, overnight, or for several nights while attending the center during the day. If patients need more than just a few days of inpatient service, they should be transferred with the understanding that the inpatient service will take over until they are ready to return to the day treatment center. Allowing a patient to be managed by both an inpatient service and a day treatment center for more than a few days causes a multitude of problems in communication that work to the detriment of all concerned. Further, if patients cannot be returned to the sole management of the day treatment center within a few days, they probably need the full-time services of the hospital. Later, when they are ready, they can be referred to the day treatment center again.

In order to have a close working relationship, it is essential to have frequent and regular meetings between the inpatient and day treatment center staffs. The inpatient staff needs to understand the limitations of the center and to see that the inpatient service is meeting a critical need by providing backup, structure, and control when needed. Otherwise, the inpatient staff may feel that the facility is being used as a dumping ground and that the day treatment staff only want "easy problems." It is also important to maintain constant communication about patients who are being kept for the weekend or overnight at the inpatient service so that both staffs are working as a team and not at cross-purposes.

Sometimes the day center staff is accused of using the hospital as "punishment." This charge may, of course, be correct; in that case, the problem should be pointed out to the staff. If a patient refuses to go along with the center's program, however, and refuses to come on a regular basis, or to participate, or to take required medication, or is a menace to himself or others, then discussing the hospital with the patient is simply pointing out reality—the hospital, after all, is the only alternative to a structured day treatment center program and the center cannot be of help unless the patient makes better use of it. Under these circumstances, hospitalization is not a punishment but a service to patients, their families, and society.

The close working relationship with the inpatient service also facilitates referrals of hospitalized patients who are not ready to return to outpatient treatment but whose hospitalization can be shortened by a full-time community program such as a day treatment center. The center staff must understand, however, that patients referred from the inpatient service frequently experience painful feelings of separation from that service and may put their "worst foot forward" to appear "too sick" for the center. Thus a patient may seem relatively intact at the inpatient service but grossly psychotic at the intake interview at the day treatment center. If this phenomenon is understood, and if good communication is maintained between the two staffs, the patient can be helped to make the transition. Otherwise, the two staffs may find themselves arguing about whether the patient is ready for the day treatment center, with a good working relationship becoming strained.

Setting a Discharge Date

Even though the patient goes home on evenings and weekends, the day treatment center is a powerful force for gratifying dependency needs. Patients often find it hard to leave and frequently will not ask to be discharged. If allowed to stay too long, however, they may become institutionalized and separation may become a major problem. Therefore, it is wise to set a discharge date, based on a careful assessment, several weeks before the patient is ready to leave the center. Once the discharge date is set, it must be a firm and final date and not subject to change unless there is some unforeseen, drastic alteration in the patient's situation, such as the death of a loved one. Establishing the discharge date results in patients no longer having to show how sick they are in order to remain in the center. If they think the discharge date *can* be changed, they are all the more likely to attempt to impress staff members with the severity of their illness. Most patients, although upset and angry at first, experience a sense of relief when the date is set. They can now begin to make meaningful plans for aftercare and for their living and work situations when they leave. It is, of course, better if the patients themselves bring up the question of leaving and ask to leave; but if they do not, it falls upon the day center staff to set the date. Frequently the patient will try to make the staff feel guilty, saying directly or indirectly, "It's cruel to send me out before I'm ready." The staff must understand that by setting the discharge date they are helping patients progress to a higher level of functioning at a time when they are ready, rather than letting them regress to a point where the process is not easily reversed.

The Center as Nucleus

Once an acute day treatment center, with a clearly defined philosophy, has been established, it can serve as the nucleus of a community network of services for the rehabilitation and management of long-term patients. Such a network establishes a support system for long-term patients in the community and eliminates the need for state hospital "rehabilitation wards." It is logical that the day treatment center should evolve as the pivotal point for such a network. The center is itself a community agency, unlike a hospital, and, naturally, develops close working relationships with other community agencies (Silverman and Val, 1975).

The day treatment center is well suited to serve as a nucleus for another reason too. Patients have come to the day center in crisis, they have been helped, and they have come to trust and have confidence in the staff. This relationship can and should be used to involve patients in an aftercare program run at least in part by the same staff—as opposed to referring them to professionals they do not know and with whom they may never follow through (Fox, 1973b). To accomplish this objective, the center could be closed to day patients one half day a week and used as an aftercare facility. (In the next section I describe such an aftercare program, one I established over fifteen years ago that is still in existence today with its basic philosophy intact.) Or the staff could run an evening aftercare program. In this case, the activity program is crucial. Such a program provides an informal, friendly atmosphere in the same place and with the same people for whom the patients still have an attachment. Consider, in contrast, the waiting room of an aftercare clinic where one simply sits until called into an office. As in the day treatment center, the activity program is only part of a comprehensive program that includes individual and group psychotherapy, vocational rehabilitation, medication, and work with the family.

An Aftercare Program

Fully as important as treating patients in the day treatment center is providing them with an adequate aftercare plan and having the resources available in the community to carry it out. For most patients with problems severe enough to warrant partial hospitalization, discharge from the day treatment center should be simply a point of transition to another phase of continuing treatment of which partial hospitalization *was* only a part, albeit a very important part. To put these concepts into action I initiated a program in 1966 when I was directing a day treatment center. Our center was closed for one afternoon a week to current day patients in order to devote itself exclusively during that afternoon to the aftercare of ex-patients (Lamb and Odenheimer, 1969). As noted earlier, this remains an ongoing program.

Most patients come to the treatment center because of problems, both acute and chronic, of psychotic or borderline psychotic proportions. Many are from the lower socioeconomic classes; many are relatively nonverbal and nonpsychologically minded (Carlson and others, 1965). A number of these patients tend to drop out of treatment prematurely. Some need to deny their dependency; others have elements of obstinacy in their character; still others are unable to trust or they fear closeness. Thus they need active pursuit by mental health professionals who will reach out and help patients return to treatment.

In these characteristics they are unlike the so-called "good" patient who seems to get top priority of outpatient treatment from many mental health professionals (Hollingshead and Redlich, 1958). Indeed, it is often difficult to "sell" most of these patients to other mental health facilities for outpatient treatment. Furthermore, many patients have strong feelings of rejection when they are referred outside of the day treatment center for aftercare. Fears of meeting new treatment staff also contribute to the difficulty of making the transition to a new agency.

For all these reasons, our attempts to refer day center patients to other treatment resources frequently resulted in no aftercare at all. Therefore much thought was given to ways of providing aftercare within the day treatment center itself by using center staff. Ex-patients had always been welcome to return to visit the day treatment center since it had opened in 1961. On one afternoon a week, set aside as open house, ex-patients were invited to come to the day treatment center, join in the activities with current patients, talk to the staff and patients, and in some cases receive psychotherapy or medication from the staff. This program was a source of considerable support for many ex-patients, especially in the period of readjustment following discharge from the day treatment center and at times of crisis.

But problems gradually became apparent. The staff found it difficult to divide its time between current day patients and aftercare patients. Indeed, there was competition between these two groups for the staff's time and attention. Moreover, because of limitations of staff time, adequate aftercare services could be offered to only a limited number of ex-patients. It was with this background that the aftercare program evolved.

The day treatment center is now closed for one afternoon a week to current day patients in order to allow the entire day center staff to focus on aftercare without distraction. The same staff members who treated the patients in the day treatment center provide a social therapy program as well as individual and group psychotherapy, couples therapy, casework with families, occupational and recreational therapy, and medications for whatever period of time is indicated. In some cases it appears, either continuously or intermittently, this may be a long-term or even lifelong contract. With this program, staff can offer aftercare services to almost all patients after discharge. They are also able to capitalize on the patients' familiarity with the setting and transference to the institution and can give them all the advantages of continuity of care. Initially, the staff was concerned that cutting the program for regular day treatment center patients to four and one-half days a week would have an adverse effect on them. To everyone's surprise, even acutely ill patients seem to do as well as previously.

The afternoon begins with a twenty- to thirty-minute meeting of all aftercare patients and staff. The group assigns tasks for the afternoon (such as cleanup), plans activities, and sometimes discusses problems of concern to them. With different patients acting as chairperson each week, many patients can take a leadership position before a group, which, at this point, averages about fifty people, including staff. This meeting has been successful in helping the group become more cohesive. Such questions as "who will clean the coffee pot?" soon became standing jokes shared by both patients and staff. This meeting also sets a tone of informality and encourages mingling.

An activity period follows the meeting. Patients usually choose activities familiar to them from the day center program. As in the day program, patients often want the staff to plan the activities while they themselves accept a role of passive compliance. Or the patients may choose activities, such as movies and lectures, in which they can be passive. With gentle urging, however, especially in the beginning, staff have been able to get the patients to assume responsibility for planning a balanced program. Most popular are table games (which provide a vehicle for social interaction in many social groups), socializing over coffee, and volleyball. These three activities have become part of the regular weekly schedule. The patients also select other activities requiring active participation, such as holiday parties, a personal grooming program for women, and occupational therapy.

Food is an important part of the program. There are refreshments each week—coffee provided by the day hospital, cake and cookies brought in by patients and staff. Potluck picnics, where the responsibility for supplying the food is shared by both patients and staff, are extremely popular with the patients and also, staff feel, therapeutic. One chronically schizophrenic young man, who at one time was quite resistant to treatment, was heard to say as he left the buffet table with his plate laden with food, "This is the kind of therapy I like!" It is important for the patients to be fed. It gives them a sense of being taken care of, which makes treatment more acceptable and attractive. At the same time, bringing in some of the food themselves helps patients gradually become more able to feed others. As one might imagine, the whole question of feeding and being fed is a core conflict with many patients in this group.

Staff usually let patients themselves decide how often they should attend the activity program. The informality of the program and the familiar faces of the staff and other patients make it fairly easy for the patient to return in times of crisis. If a patient appears reluctant to come and if the staff thinks attendance is especially important, staff may "prescribe" regular attendance and participation—especially in the period of transition immediately after discharge from the day treatment center. For those who attend regularly, the program is like a half-day a week day treatment center.

Staff attempt to tailor the services to each patient's specific needs. For some patients, medication and the activity program seem to be the therapy of choice; more intensive treatment and intervention are given at times of crisis only. This group includes a number of patients whose relationship is primarily with the institution. Several patients who in the past developed "transference psychoses" in more intensive individual psychotherapy, which could not be worked through and led to return to hospital or acute day treatment, have done extremely well in such a program. For patients for whom staff feel group therapy is indicated, groups meet for an hour every other week. Some patients and their spouses are seen in couples therapy.

Employment and vocational services are emphasized as an important part of the program both in the day treatment center and in aftercare. Many patients in aftercare continue to be seen by the program's vocational counselors. Many are involved full-time or part-time on work placement or in a sheltered workshop.

Despite the emphasis on group and social therapy I believe that individual therapy on a regular, ongoing basis is extremely important for many of these patients. As in the day treatment center itself, the group and social therapies on the one hand and individual therapy on the other are not mutually exclusive; rather they complement and supplement each other if an individualized aftercare plan takes into account the patient's particular needs and problems. Individual therapy need not be a fifty-minute hour nor weekly; it may be twenty minutes every two weeks or once a month. For many patients there is no substitute for the one-to-one relationship with a therapist who understands the dynamics of the case and can apply this knowledge in a practical way by helping patients work through current and past conflicts and by giving specific kinds of advice. Again, this is not working through the core conflicts in an attempt to "cure" schizophrenia; it is reality-oriented therapy or ego-building therapy geared to handling situational and interpersonal stresses that might, without help, overwhelm the patient. This is considered more than supportive therapy; it is hoped that patients will learn how to cope with their problems and in time will need less help from staff in handling stressful situations.

As described earlier, the activity program plays fully as important a role as any of the other treatment modalities in the day treatment center. In many ways it sets the tone and establishes a therapeutic atmosphere. In the aftercare program, too, emphasis is placed on occupational therapy and recreational therapy. The program is seen as one in which all the treatment modalities—individual and group psychotherapy (properly used), occupational and recreational therapy, social therapy, medication—play an important role.

A study by Linn and others (1979) of day treatment centers used for aftercare revealed that those characterized by more occupational therapy and a sustained nonthreatening environment had better results in terms of delaying relapse and reducing symptoms than those characterized by more professional staff hours, group therapy, and a philosophy of high patient turnover. This study, then, supports a philosophy of emphasizing the activity therapies while guarding against the pitfalls of psychotherapy discussed earlier in this chapter.

For patients who find it difficult to ask for help, especially when they are in crisis and most in need of it, dropping in to visit an aftercare activity program run by the day treatment center allows them to present themselves for help while rationalizing that they "just came back to visit." The staff comes to know the patients and their individual patterns of reacting to stress during their stay in the day treatment center. Thus, staff members can often readily identify the early signs of exacerbation of illness while chatting informally with patients or observing them in activities. Crises can thus be averted, or patients can be readmitted while their problems can still be easily managed or resolved.

All patients in aftercare are assigned to both a psychiatrist and another staff member. If the psychiatrist is the primary therapist, the other staff member is usually called in only when the family must be involved. If a nonpsychiatrist is the primary therapist, the psychiatrist may only write prescriptions and not be involved unless there are special circumstances. Patients are aware that both a psychiatrist and another staff member are assigned to their case; staff say this knowledge is very supportive to patients even though they may contact the secondary staff member infrequently or not at all.

The philosophy of the aftercare program is an extension of the day center's approach to treatment. Staff want their patients to be able to take responsibility and to give to others and the program. When they can do so, they are frequently then able to apply these attitudes in their lives outside the program with a consequent improvement in their level of functioning and their self-esteem. Staff work to make the aftercare program a milieu in which the attitudes of active participation and taking responsibility are taken for granted and communicated to patients not only by staff but also by other patients. Sometimes these issues are explicitly discussed in the group meeting.

This aftercare program provides considerable support, but not on the scale of a full-time day treatment center that would over long periods of time foster dependency to an unnecessary and unhealthy degree. At the beginning the staff was concerned that the half-day a week program might itself foster undue dependency. But it was found that only about a fourth of active aftercare patients come regularly, stay the full afternoon, and appear to be permanent aftercare fixtures. Considering the neediness and the degree of illness of this group, a half-day a week of ongoing day treatment appears to be quite appropriate. Those needing additional service can receive it in a vocational or social rehabilitation program (see Chapter Fourteen). Some patients attend aftercare less than they should or drop out prematurely, but most patients do not overprescribe for themselves in terms of treatment in the aftercare program.

At first, staff also feared they might be overburdened when responsibility for a multitude of needy, dependent aftercare patients was added to their regular caseload in the day treatment center. This has not been the case. Patients seem to make good use of the program, but they do not drain staff—perhaps because the staff emphasizes active participation and acceptance of responsibility, perhaps because the staff's support helps patients make better use of their own strengths, perhaps because of the ongoing collaboration with vocational rehabilitation services and the sheltered workshop.

Staff say they have been able to provide most of their patients with a valuable continuation of their day hospital treatment—a continuation that helps them maintain, and in many cases, improve, their level of functioning and sense of well-being in the community. Furthermore, staff have found it rewarding to participate in the ongoing treatment of patients, rather than simply catching a prolonged glimpse of them in the specialized setting of the day treatment center.

Forming the Network

In addition to setting up an aftercare program in the day treatment center, the center staff should make referrals to, and maintain liaison with, vocational rehabilitation agencies, halfway houses, satellite housing programs, board-and-care home operators and their consultants, and social rehabilitation programs. Thus a network of services is created that can meet the vocational, housing, and social rehabilitation needs, the crises, and the continuing treatment needs of long-term patients.

It is crucial that efforts be coordinated. Coordination not only increases the effectiveness of each agency but also leads to consensus among the various agencies about a treatment plan so that agencies will not be working at cross-purposes. Communication about a patient's progress or lack of it in one area may enable professionals from another agency to modify their own work with the patient. Liaison among various agencies should be regularly scheduled, not merely "as needed" or only at times of crisis (Lamb, 1971a). A member from the workshop staff may attend the halfway house's weekly staff meeting, a member of the halfway house may attend the aftercare staff's weekly meeting, and so on. When liaison is not regularly scheduled, communication becomes a sometime thing—to the detriment of the patient, the treatment plan, and agency interrelationships.

The web of relationships proposed here gives professionals and paraprofessionals from a number of diverse services a sense of cohesiveness. It helps cut through bureaucratic red tape and facilitates referrals and communication generally—staff members from one agency know whom to call in other agencies. Because the staff members in each agency know there is a network of supportive services to back them up, they are more confident about undertaking the treatment of difficult patients. Close coordination gives agency staffs intimate knowledge of one another's operations and problems; that knowledge, in turn, facilitates further collaboration, and staffs learn to use other agencies' services more effectively and appropriately.

But simply referring patients to these agencies is not enough. Identifying goals is important in every part of the network of services. If a patient is referred to a vocational workshop, for instance, both the patient and all staff members concerned should understand why. Is the workshop to assess the patient's ability to work? Is it to resolve problems with authority figures or coworkers on the job? The workshop staff needs to know if they are to do more than simply expose the patient to work. If the goal is indefinite sheltered employment, then this objective should be clarified so that large amounts of energy are not used to pursue unrealistic goals.

There is often disagreement between referring mental health professionals and the staffs of workshops, halfway houses, and other facilities as to what the main goals are and how they are to be achieved. Disagreements should be handled at regularly scheduled liaison meetings, during which both general policy issues and individual clients are discussed, so that patients are not torn by conflicts among the several agencies working with them.

Another principle that should be applied throughout the entire network of services is that *all* appropriate referrals should be taken, no matter how unappealing the patient might seem. An obese, middle-aged, nonverbal, uneducated patient with body odor is just as deserving of services as anyone else. In fact, one of the most frequent shortcomings in community mental health programs is their tendency to treat patients who are enjoyable to treat rather than those who may need the services most (Hogarty, 1971).

A Final Word

We have seen how a short-term, goal-oriented day treatment center can provide a true alternative to hospitalization for long-term patients. This prospect is especially likely if the center has clearly defined, time-limited goals, if it is oriented to the psychodynamics of the here and now, if it has a comprehensive program including

individual and group psychotherapy and a meaningful activity program, if it uses adequate dosages of psychoactive medications, if it
emphasizes work with the family, and if it clearly defines staff roles
and works closely with an inpatient service.

The day treatment center also can serve as the pivotal point
for a network of coordinated services, including long-term aftercare,
vocational and social rehabilitation, and therapeutic housing. The
center capitalizes on the relationships formed with patients during
acute crisis; it is hard to duplicate a patient's trust in the agency and
the staff that have helped him when he was most desperate and most
needy. Long-term patients need the sense of security that comes from
knowing there is a support system in the community with a full
range of services that can sustain them in what often seems to be a
frightening world full of overwhelming demands. With such a system, we can not only supplant state hospitals but also help long-
term patients become, insofar as they are able, part of the
mainstream of the community.

❧ Fourteen ☙

Social Rehabilitation

One theme of this book is that, insofar as possible, long-term patients should be helped to cast off the patient role and see themselves as citizens like any others in the community. While recognizing this is the ideal and not often fully attainable, I feel we should strive to normalize the environment in which they work and play. Thus, we should try to set up programs outside of mental health settings. Long-term patients can become as dependent on a community mental health center as they were on the hospital.

The whole process of acquiring social competence (usually called social rehabilitation) lends itself readily to this approach. As will be shown throughout this chapter, the helping persons with whom the patient has direct contact should be teachers, volunteers, recreation department personnel, and college students. Long-term patients need maximum contact with regular members of the community. Otherwise, they are led to feel they can associate only with other patients and mental health professionals and paraprofessionals specifically trained and paid to take care of them—as was the case in the hospital. In the social rehabilitation process, as distinguished from other aspects of treatment and rehabilitation, mental health professionals can best serve as consultants. Unfortunately, it has been my observation that many mental health professionals are reluctant to limit their role in this way; they want to do the social

Note: This is a revised version of a chapter by the author from H. R. Lamb and Associates, *Community Survival for Long-Term Patients* (San Francisco: Jossey-Bass, 1976).

189

rehabilitation themselves. In such instances patients lose out doubly: They are deprived of contact with persons outside of mental
health settings, and they are deprived of treatment that these trained
professionals could otherwise have provided.

Social Rehabilitation in a School Setting

When the many thousands of long-term psychiatric patients
began streaming out of the state hospitals into the community, it
quickly became clear that they were woefully deficient in the basic
skills of everyday living. More recent experience in community
mental health programs, with young chronic schizophrenics, has
revealed similar problems even though these patients have not spent
long years in state hospitals. Their deficits in ego functioning include not being able to achieve mastery over their environment.
Much of their difficulty in adjusting to the community has to do
with not knowing the everyday essentials—managing their money
and budgeting, how to use banking services, how to utilize the resources available to them in the community, how to use their leisure
time, the fundamentals of nutrition, meal planning, and shopping,
how to use public transportation, the essentials of grooming, personal hygiene, and sex education, and the basic social amenities that
make the difference between a life of isolation and having friends.
For many patients, knowledge and skills in these matters not only
make a great difference in the quality of their lives but make the
difference between being able to live independently or semi-
independently in the community and living in a hospital or at a low
level of functioning in a residential care home.

Some argue that the most effective way to impart these skills
systematically to long-term schizophrenic patients is to use an educational model—that is, to set up classes and to have a curriculum
(Glasscote and others, 1971; Ludwig, 1971; Spiegler and Agigian,
1977). Unfortunately, these programs have been established in mental health settings such as hospitals, day treatment centers, and aftercare programs. But keeping long-term patients in a mental health
setting promotes dependency on the setting rather than independence. These considerations led me to set up a social rehabilitation

program to teach the basic skills of everyday living not only on an educational model but in an educational setting.

It should be said at the outset that programs such as this are not for everyone. We saw in Chapter Four that about a fourth of board-and-care home residents were emotionally unable or simply unwilling to walk one block to attend a social rehabilitation program; another fourth attended only briefly before dropping out. In my view, the educational model is the most appropriate for teaching basic living skills, but for a sizable number of patients the teacher must come to facilities such as board-and-care homes. This has been done successfully.

But let us return to the social rehabilitation program I developed in an educational setting. The local high school district was approached and readily agreed to sponsor the course as a regular part of its adult education program and pay for the teacher. We looked for a credentialed teacher who would be flexible enough to teach a group of students who present somewhat different problems than those normally encountered in the classroom. Since the teacher we hired had a great deal of experience teaching classes of emotionally handicapped children, he was prepared to deal with crises in his classroom and with students whose emotional problems interfere with learning. The course was entitled "Personal Growth Education." We would have preferred to use a regular school classroom, but daytime classroom space was not available for the eight hours a week we needed for this course. However, the local chapter of the American Red Cross made one of their classrooms available to us for the first year. In the second year the course was moved to a community recreation center. At both locations there was no charge for the classroom; and at both the atmosphere was definitely noninstitutional. Before each course, the teacher speaks to aftercare personnel and social clubs for long-term patients. Many of the students have had the course recommended to them by their therapists. Moreover, the course is offered in the regular adult-school catalog. But however the potential students have heard about the course, they enroll for it as they would for any other adult-school course.

Encouraging Student Involvement. A key element in this course is encouraging student involvement. The first class of each course in Personal Growth Education is devoted to having the ten to twelve students make up a "needs list." The students are asked what they see as their needs in terms of the knowledge and skills of everyday living. All of the needs they mention are listed on the blackboard, and in the ensuing discussion the class decides which topics are most important for the group as a whole. They then assign priorities, and the topics receiving priority are given the greatest emphasis during the course. It is further understood that the needs list can be revised as the course goes along, and the list is posted where it can be seen at each class. Thus the teacher and students together draw up the curriculum. The importance of the students' participation cannot be overestimated, for in addition to learning the specifics of the course they also learn to take responsibility. For those who have spent long periods in state hospitals or other institutions where most decisions are made for them, responsibility is a new experience. Even for the students who have not yet become "institutionalized," the knowledge that they have responsibility for what happens in the classroom is translatable to other areas of their lives. Many long-term patients feel that they cannot exercise any control over what befalls them and have, therefore, no responsibility for their fate; they see themselves as victims. Learning that they can take responsibility for what happens in a class thus becomes especially meaningful, for it helps them see that they have control over what happens to them elsewhere too. What occurred in the classroom happened because of *them* and not simply because of what the teacher said and did.

Because students set course priorities, the curriculum of Personal Growth Education differs somewhat from group to group. One group may emphasize nutrition and planning meals and managing one's money; another group may want to make better use of leisure time and learn basic etiquette and what is and is not acceptable interpersonal behavior. Each course, however, covers all of these subjects to a greater or lesser degree, taking into account both student priorities and the fact that one group may need to start at the most elementary level while another may be somewhat more advanced.

From Patient to Student. One of the most important aspects of this course is that the students are called "students," they see themselves as students, and they have the identity of students. Since the teacher is not a mental health professional and the setting is an educational one, not a mental health one, long-term patients begin to see that they can be like other people in the community, doing things that other people do, such as going to school. When they meet people and are asked what they are doing, many of them say, "I'm going to school" or "I'm taking a class in personal growth education." The prospect of returning to school may create apprehension at first, for many long-term patients have had previous negative experiences with the educational system or lack confidence in their ability to meet the demands of an educational setting. But when they get there and find that the course is relevant to their needs and that they can handle it, their self-esteem is enhanced and they feel more secure in their ability to handle the demands of the world.

The course also helps long-term patients realize that the basic skills of everyday living are learned skills, not abilities or talents magically bestowed on others but not on them. Many long-term patients seem to have a fantasy that they are different from other people—that others have acquired these skills in some unknown way. The students discover that others too have had to learn these skills, though perhaps under different circumstances; these are not skills that one is born with. As the mystique of coping with the world is taken away, students learn that they too can acquire the ability to "make it."

Classes are held four hours a day (with breaks excluded, a little over three hours of actual class time) two days a week, and the course lasts a full semester. The full course is offered twice a year, and a brief summer session is offered as well. Some students are allowed to repeat the course if they wish and the teacher feels it is appropriate. The small class size of ten to twelve people is a key factor. It gives the teacher a chance to know the students well, which is extremely important in learning how to help each student individually. Further, the small group allows for much interaction with fellow students. When budgeting is studied, for instance, each student draws up a budget and then the class discusses it. This technique is supportive in that all the students go through the experience together. Furthermore, there is an opportunity for much give-and-take in what quickly becomes a close-knit group; students get feedback from one another in terms of what they did right, what they did wrong, and where they can improve.

The topic of budgeting also demonstrates how the practical results of the course can be evaluated. After each student has drawn up a budget, continued class discussions provide the opportunity to observe how students do over the remainder of the month and the following months. For many students, reaching the end of the month with a few dollars left is a new experience. In view of the fact that most students receive SSI and that those living in residential care facilities may have less than sixty dollars a month for all their personal needs, this accomplishment is indeed impressive. Similarly, in the ongoing discussions following the classes on nutrition, meal planning, and shopping, the teacher gets a clear picture of what changes, if any, are taking place in the students' eating habits. Feedback from therapists indicates that the course has been especially helpful for patients moving from hospitals, halfway houses, and residential care facilities to independent living situations.

Initial reactions to the course frequently reveal what the students have become used to in mental health settings and how they have to shift gears in moving to an educational setting. In drawing up the needs list, for instance, many students at first request sightseeing trips, such as going to see a new, architecturally unique hotel or taking outings to the park. They have to adjust to a setting where their activity must be purposeful and part of the educational process. Though many students have spent years in mental health settings, where they have become overly dependent, most are able to make the transition during the first few weeks—perhaps because many have a deep need for purposeful activity. Students tell us later that they are sick of sightseeing trips and often requested these excursions simply because they thought their requests fit the pattern expected of them.

The transition presents problems for mental health professionals too. When Personal Growth Education was set up, a referral form was designed with room for past history, type of living situation, and comments by the therapist. At the bottom of the form the prospective student signed a release so the therapist could give this information to the teacher. We now see that this procedure evolved from our own discomfort in operating outside a mental health setting. While therapists are now encouraged to suggest to their patients that they take this course, the students simply report to the course and fill in the brief personal information form themselves. The original procedure was not only unnecessary but gave students the feeling they were involved in yet another mental health setting. Occasions will, of course, arise when the teacher feels the need to talk to parents or significant others in the student's life. In such a situation, the teacher asks the student's permission; if the teacher wishes to talk with the therapist, he obtains a release of information that allows the therapist to talk with him about the student. This is done, however, as infrequently as possible.

After initial negotiations and organization of the course, this project costs the local mental health program nothing more than an average of one and one-half hours per week of the time of a mental health professional. The student pays five dollars for the registration fee. Courses like this compensate for the ego deficits and experiential lacks of long-term patients. Moreover, they serve as an example of how to reintegrate the long-term patient at minimum cost to community mental health programs—if they are taught as classes, by teachers, and outside a mental health setting. In these times of scarce mental health funds, we must look for new ways of involving other systems in bringing needed services to long-term patients.

The Personal Growth Education teacher has easy access to mental health consultation and uses it. But the course is his. And when the teacher feels the need for resource people, he contacts people outside the mental health field, such as a home economics teacher (planning meals), a police captain (understanding the functions of the police), or a librarian (using the library). As an incidental benefit of the class, students receive credit toward a high school diploma if they do not already have one. But, more important, students acquire a new identity, that of *student*, and feel they can participate in activities outside of mental health centers just like others in the community. That identity, combined with the information imparted in the course, helps the student progress beyond the mental health system.

Again, patients must be capable and willing to venture forth from their asylums in settings such as board-and-care homes. But this program is probably no more demanding than going to a day treatment center. I believe the educational model and use of teachers rather than mental health professionals is a sound policy for patients at all levels of functioning and in a variety of settings.

Using Recreation Departments and Libraries

Many mental health centers are making greater use of other facilities in their own communities. They have found recreation departments and libraries receptive to programs for long-term patients. Recreation departments have set up a variety of athletic activities, classes in sewing, needlepoint, and macrame, and also photography clubs specifically for long-term patients. Sometimes these activities are jointly led by mental health professionals and members of the recreation department staff. But the more desirable programs, in my view, are those run solely by recreation department personnel with only consultation from mental health personnel. For many long-term patients, these activities can be transitional in leading to the regular programs of the recreation department in which members of the general public participate. To facilitate this transition, programs designed for the general public should make special efforts to help the hesitant feel welcome. Indeed, such efforts are important for many in the community other than long-term patients.

The public library can also be a rich resource. Many librarians are extremely adept at leading literary discussion and current events groups for long-term patients. Again, mental health consultation to the library staff is important to the success of these programs.

Friendship Centers

A concept that has been effective in helping long-term patients acquire social competence is that of the friendship center, sometimes called a "friendship club" or "friendship circle." The friendship center is staffed by volunteers and often is sponsored by the local mental health association. Its purpose is to bring long-term patients together under circumstances in which they can interact with one another and with "normal" members of the community—namely, the volunteers. One of the center's goals is to reduce the isolation of these patients and help them to improve their social skills and be comfortable in social situations. Another goal is to help members learn how to use their leisure time, with the hope that they will increase their social interaction and use of community resources outside the program. The usual pattern is for the center to hold meetings once a week for about half a day, often from 10 A.M. to 2 P.M. and usually in a church. The meetings center around social and recreational activities. In a typical program, mornings are set aside for such activities as crafts, table games, cooking, listening to music, and just visiting. Lunch is a "brown bag" affair, except on special occasions, when everyone shares in a potluck lunch. Business meetings, with a chairperson elected each month from the group, follow lunch. These meetings promote group cohesiveness and help members become more active in planning their activities and making decisions about their center. Afternoons are devoted to group activities planned at previous meetings—a trip to the park for a picnic or a nature walk, for example, or trips to the county fair and local tourist attractions. A key element in the concept of friendship centers is that they be staffed entirely by volunteers. Mental health professionals usually serve as consultants, but they do not participate in the program itself.

Experience has shown that a paid coordinator of volunteers is essential, especially if the sponsoring agency contemplates a network of several centers. The coordinator need not be, and usually is not, a mental health professional. This person should have skills in community organization, an ability to communicate enthusiasm, and a willingness to provide support to the volunteers when they feel anxious about a situation in the center.

The volunteers are recruited by the mental health association; most are housewives, although occasionally there are male volunteers. The volunteers must be carefully screened by the coordinator, perhaps with the assistance of the mental health consultant, so that those selected have the interpersonal skills necessary to work with long-term psychiatric patients. It is usually possible to attract volunteers by obtaining publicity through local newspapers and church bulletins.

About once a month, after the friendship center closes, all the volunteers from that center meet to discuss how the center is going, how to further increase community involvement, various problems with the members that have come up during the month, how they were handled, and alternative ways they might have been handled. The consultant usually participates in this meeting. Each center has a volunteer chairperson who presides over the monthly meeting and is generally the person in charge while the center is open.

Sometimes the church at which meetings are held becomes very involved in sponsoring or cosponsoring the program, in which case a large proportion of the volunteers may be members of the church. Or the church may be active in initiating the program. An excellent example is the Community Organization for Personal Enrichment (COPE) program, a high-quality social rehabilitation program run by volunteers who have been trained by the program (Cutler and Beigel, 1978). The COPE program is a joint venture of the Tucson Metropolitan Ministry of the Methodist Church and the Southern Arizona Mental Health Center; the latter also provides mental health consultation. Each COPE patient is, in addition, under the care of a mental health center.

It is essential to have a training program before volunteers begin working in a center. Most training is handled by the mental health consultant in conjunction with the coordinator. The training program need not be extensive, but it should include orientation to the various mental health facilities and programs in the community and should cover some of the rudiments of working with persons with emotional problems.

The mental health consultant performs an essential function by helping friendship center volunteers handle the everyday problems that arise in relating to long-term patients. These problems loom large for volunteers, who, without guidance and support, feel insecure and anxious and frequently flee to a "less threatening" volunteer activity. For instance, a volunteer in a friendship center may wonder what her degree of responsibility is if a member runs away. A simple statement from the consultant that the volunteer's responsibility is to work in the center and does not include being certain that members remain on the premises can be very reassuring. Further, the consultant lessens the volunteer's sense of guilt ("It's my fault that he ran away"), which might otherwise be overwhelming and drive the volunteer away. Another volunteer may be concerned about her responsibility if a member purposely harms himself. Again, the volunteers are helping to run an activity center; but they cannot take responsibility for controlling or stopping grossly pathological behavior, and they need to know this. If the member's behavior is grossly inappropriate or out of control, the volunters should be encouraged to call a responsible person—a parent, a spouse, or an operator of a residential care facility—to come and get the member. And they should know that they can refuse to take him back until he can behave more appropriately.

The question of how to motivate members in a friendship center frequently leaves volunteers in a quandary. Here the consultant can be helpful by encouraging one-to-one contact when necessary and by helping the volunteers understand that some members simply do not have the capacity to participate on their own at first. The volunteers can be helpful in such cases by approaching the member and taking the initiative. Peer pressure is another effective way of motivating the members to engage not only in small-group activities such as arts and crafts but also in large-group activities such as cleanup. Volunteers need to understand that many long-term patients are reluctant to exert peer pressure on their fellow members. Encouraging peer pressure is often a valuable technique for the volunteer.

Many volunteers ask how to recognize progress in a member. Sometimes they expect too much too soon from long-term patients. The volunteer needs to understand that for many members, just being able to leave their residential care facilities or their families and come to the center is an accomplishment.

Mental health consultants can be helpful to volunteers in much the same way as they help the administrators and staff of residential care facilities (see Chapter Five for the discussion of setting limits and understanding the mental health system).

Drop-In Social Centers

Sometimes we in mental health seem to feel that patients spring into existence during working hours and go to some never-

never land in between. We pay too little attention to how the long weekend and evening hours are spent. For most of us, evenings and weekends are among our most satisfying times, but for the long-term patient with few resources and even fewer contacts, these are the really depressing and upsetting times. The drop-in social center is designed to meet these "after hours" needs of long-term patients.

Such a center, like the friendship center, should be staffed by volunteers and should not be located in a community mental health center or hospital. It can be organized and sponsored by the local mental health association or some other private, nonprofit agency. And, as in the case of the friendship center, a paid coordinator is crucial. The center need not operate twenty-four hours a day, but it should be open evenings and weekends. The drop-in center is a place where patients can go to talk or play games such as table tennis, cards, and backgammon. The atmosphere is informal— comfortable furniture, a coffee pot always going, a minimum of rules. Although one of the primary goals is to promote socialization, patients are free to choose their own level of interaction. If a person simply wants to listen to music or read the newspaper and magazines that are available, the center is still providing a valuable service. It should be remembered that although long-term patients may feel lonely and need to be with people, they may at the same time need to maintain social distance, at least at first. Although the center should be staffed by volunteers, mental health professionals should be involved as consultants and a professional should be on call whenever the center is open.

Unfortunately, drop-in social centers have a tendency to grow and expand in ways that defeat their primary purpose of being small, informal, noninstitutional gathering places. The drop-in social center should not become a treatment center. The informal, in-the-community atmosphere is lost if the center becomes a place where the person also receives therapy and medication. The center must not become professionalized. The entire character of such a center changes when professionals take over. Moreover, the center must guard against falling victim to the "edifice complex," with larger and larger and more and more expensive buildings. Along with such structures comes the inevitable need to justify them with additional programs.

Companion Programs

A number of communities have established programs based on prolonged one-to-one contact between volunteer and patient. As in the case of the friendship center, the volunteers are carefully selected and trained. The basic intent is to give the patient the experience of a warm, supportive relationship with a stable, well-adjusted member of the community—an experience the patient sorely needs and may never have experienced. The program takes into account the needs of each patient and the personalities of the various patients and volunteers. Volunteers are then matched with patients on the basis of compatibility to provide the best opportunity for a therapeutic result. In the program in Marin County, California, the volunteer makes a six-month commitment to the relationship; in other programs the commitment may be only three months. Frequently, however, by the time the formal commitment has ended, the relationship has turned into a mutual friendship and continues as such. The volunteer companion may spend anywhere from four to ten hours a week with the patient, depending on what is deemed appropriate and necessary. Some of the time is spent just talking; some is spent going to various social and recreational activities. In some instances, and especially with more regressed patients, the companion provides help with transportation, shopping, and other daily-living activities. Whenever possible, public transportation is used so that the patient does not regard the volunteer as a chauffeur. It is important that the patient see the volunteer as a person who does things with him, not for him; too much dependence on the companion is thus discouraged. As in the other programs described in this chapter, the long-term patient is given the opportunity to relate to someone who is not a patient or a mental health professional. It is hoped that the volunteer will provide a model for the patient in terms of coping and problem solving, acquiring social competence, and learning to use community resources.

The Marin County Companion Program initially gives its volunteers a three-week orientation, with six sessions of two or three hours each. To provide ongoing support, the two staff members make themselves available to the volunteers for consultation twenty-four hours a day. In addition, they hold evening group meetings once a week for two hours so that volunteers can discuss problems they have encountered. Each volunteer is required to attend at least one group meeting every two weeks. The Marin County program has forty to fifty active volunteer companions at any given time.

Some companion programs aim to provide enough support to those in crisis so that hospitalization or admission to a day treatment center can be averted. When this is the goal, the companions are much more highly trained; in fact, they are considered paraprofessionals and are paid. They may be with the patient in the patient's own living situation twenty-four hours a day until the crisis is past.

Harnessing the Enthusiasm of Students

One of the greatest resources for providing social rehabilitation to long-term patients is the millions of college and university students, both undergraduate and graduate, who would be willing to help. Unfortunately, this vast potential is relatively untapped. Students have youthful enthusiasm and energy that can be contagious to both patients and staff. Moreover, they often possess an openness that is refreshing. If carefully selected, students are able to make contact, in a variety of settings, with regressed, withdrawn patients as few others can.

Since nearly every community has at least a nearby junior college, this resource is available almost everywhere. Students are motivated by an idealism that has not yet become jaded. Further, many need community service experience to their credit when applying to professional and graduate schools. It is also possible to give college credit for working with psychiatric patients as part of an organized community service program; a very successful program has been carried out at various campuses of the California State University system: the Educational Participation in Communities (EPIC) program.

Like all volunteers, of course, students need consultation, supervision, and support.

There are other benefits in using students as volunteers. If, with our help, they gain a greater understanding of the mentally ill, and become comfortable with them, the groundwork will have been laid for increased acceptance of the mentally ill as these student volunteers move on to take their place in society.

A Final Word

Several common threads run through this chapter. Long-term patients can best acquire social competence if their primary contact is with regular members of the community. They should spend as much time as possible in settings used by the community at large. Programs based on these premises—whether they are structured as courses taught by teachers, friendship centers run by housewife volunteers, or activities staffed by college students—all help integrate long-term patients into the community. In my opinion, mental health professionals can best serve the cause of social rehabilitation by serving as consultants. Except in specific treatment situations—such as an acute day treatment center or a once weekly aftercare program set up to provide the patient's primary treatment program including medication and individual and group psychotherapy (see Chapter Thirteen)—mental health professionals should yield the field to community members such as teachers, recreation department personnel, and volunteers including students.

⌘ Fifteen ⌘

Avoiding Staff Burnout

In the preceding chapters, we have focused primarily on patients, their families, reactions of society, and methods of treatment. All these concerns take their toll on the mental health worker, however, so in this chapter we turn our attention to what is one of the caregiver's overriding problems: burnout.

The realization that many tens of thousands of long-term, severely disabled patients now in the community have been given very low priority by community mental health centers and most other social and community agencies (Hogarty, 1971; Kirk and Therrien, 1975) has led to a flurry of activity to serve these patients. In some cases, this has come about because of pressure from funding sources; in other cases, there has been a heightened awareness of past neglect and, perhaps, feelings of guilt. But simply increasing services to long-term patients without an in-depth understanding of their needs and capabilities and without having a sound underlying conceptual framework for their treatment has created many new problems. In particular, large numbers of new staff have been enlisted in these efforts without a realistic conception of what they can expect to accomplish. Most of them enter the field with enthusiasm and good intentions. But in time, perhaps a year or two, they have become "burned out": They have lost their enthusiasm; they no longer like their contact with long-term patients; they are bored;

Note: This chapter is a revised and expanded version of a paper entitled "Staff Burnout in Work with Long-Term Patients," *Hospital & Community Psychiatry*, 1979, *30*, 396–398.

they feel frustrated and resentful. Worst of all, they have become ineffective.

The literature now abounds with theories about staff burnout in a variety of settings. Burnout has been attributed to high patient/staff ratios, to long work hours, to lack of a sense of autonomy, to working primarily with the chronically and severely ill, and having to spend all or most of one's time on the job in direct contact with patients without opportunities for other tasks or "timeouts" (Pines and Maslach, 1978). Some believe that staff burnout results from being given responsibility without the authority or resources needed to get the job done and a lack of recognition for one's efforts and accomplishments (Emener, 1979). Role conflict and role ambiguity have been identified as factors that contribute to burnout in community mental health (Kahn, 1978; Cherniss, 1980). In the case of role conflict, one receives two or more conflicting sets of information as to what is required on the job. In the case of role ambiguity, one has insufficient information about the job: its scope and responsibilities, how to do it adequately, the opportunities for advancement, what coworkers expect, and how supervisors evaluate staff. The priority given in our society and in the helping professions to the crisis model, with its emphasis on resolution of emergencies and cure, has been cited as a major cause of burnout for those who are called upon to deal with chronic illness and provide supportive care (Mendel, 1979). All the factors in this far from complete list undoubtedly play a part. This chapter focuses on some additional issues that I have found to be of particular importance in causing staff burnout with long-term severely disabled patients.

A major cause of burnout has been the failure of mental health professionals to clearly recognize that there are many different kinds of "long-term patients" and that these patients vary greatly in the degree to which they can be rehabilitated. They differ in ego strength (the ability to cope with stress) and in motivation. The severely disabled differ also in the kinds of stress and pressure they can handle. Some who are amenable to social rehabilitation cannot handle the stresses of vocational rehabilitation and vice versa. What may appear to be, at first glance, a homogeneous group turns out to be a group that ranges from persons who can tolerate almost no stress at all to those who can, with some assistance, cope with most of life's demands. Thus, for some long-term patients, competitive employment, independent living, and a high level of social functioning are realistic goals; for others, just maintaining their present level of functioning should be considered a success (Solomon and others, 1980).

The failure of mental health staff to recognize or accept these differences creates major problems. It is tremendously frustrating for staff to attempt to do something faster than it can be done or, worse yet, to attempt to do something that cannot be done at all. If staff fail to see that they cannot rehabilitate all long-term patients and, even then, that a large proportion can be rehabilitated only to some degree, they may attempt to bring *all* long-term patients up to the same high level of achievement. This effort can lead only to staff frustration and is, in my opinion, a major factor in staff burnout.

Overselling Rehabilitation

The great majority of the severely mentally disabled have been ignored and offered few services. Unfortunately, when mental health professionals finally do turn their attention to the severely disabled, the result is all too frequently a shift from neglect to over-enthusiastic attempts at rehabilitation and unrealistic expectations. There is the danger that we may discredit the whole idea of rehabilitation if we oversell it and make promises we cannot keep. Now that we are finally beginning to interest mental health professionals in the treatment and rehabilitation of long-term patients, our goals need to be attainable if we expect staff to undertake what has heretofore been considered a low-status, low-prestige, unrewarding activity.

Above all, staff should accept the slow pace at which most long-term patients can progress (Allen, 1974). We are not surprised when intensive psychotherapy with persons possessing greater ego strength takes years to achieve character change, relief of symptoms, and alteration of pathological interpersonal reactions. Yet we are frequently dismayed when the long-term severely disabled take years to progress in social and vocational rehabilitation.

Further, when patients attempt activities and "fail" or drop out, they often receive the blame, either explicitly or by innuendo.

But the problem may really lie in the fact that activities within the patient's capabilities—social rehabilitation programs undemanding of social skills, for example, or low-pressure work activity programs—were not available.

Normalization and Realistic Expectations

The concept of normalization can pose another problem. Certainly we want the long-term patient's social milieu, living situation, and work situation to be as much like that of any other citizen as possible. We hope that the patients' condition will not set them any further apart from others in our society than necessary. But we frequently forget that normalization is the ideal and that, for many, normalization is possible to only a limited extent. Some long-term patients may need to live in a sheltered living situation that is by its very nature segregated. They may be able to participate only in low-key community activities specifically geared to them. Their manner and appearance, even with optimal doses of psychoactive medications and optimal amounts of psychosocial treatment, may set them apart (Lamb, 1979b).

Failure to understand these matters has led many mental health professionals to push long-term patients beyond their capabilities, at times to the point of failure. In so doing, staff have undermined their patients' sense of autonomy and mastery. There is also the opposite danger of getting caught up in patients' perceptions of themselves as helpless and chronic, thereby colluding with them in disregarding their own ego strengths. Staff should have skills to detect these strengths and the hidden motivation for growth that often manifests itself in distorted or indirect ways.

Maintaining realistic expectations of our patients is necessary if we are to work effectively with them. But to what extent should we push them? Are there times when we push them because we have unrealistic expectations and fail to realize that there are many different kinds of long-term patients and wide variations in their ego strength, in their potential, and in their degrees of competence? I feel we should attempt to sell patients on involvement in treatment and rehabilitation; if we think they can make progress, we should let them know we think so. It is often useful to convey the message that they will think better of themselves if they strive to reach their potential. But our efforts will be hampered if we push all patients because we feel they can be rehabilitated or because we are getting social and administrative pressure to produce results.

Without strong pressure to attain results, mental health staff can find working with long-term patients more gratifying. If staff can take satisfaction from simply improving the quality of a patient's life without necessarily increasing his or her level of functioning, for instance, they can enjoy contact with the patient more. Staff can learn how patients feel about their lives and can help them achieve a sense of trust or even closeness, a new experience for many. But in order to do this, staff should be spared the pressure to produce what cannot be produced—namely, rehabilitation of patients beyond their potential, a pressure which is passed on to patients and which, sooner or later, will only drive them away or cause staff to reject them out of a sense of frustration.

Social and vocational rehabilitation can significantly enhance the quality of life for many long-term patients. In some cases, rehabilitation can lead to a full and satisfying social life, competitive employment, or both. For many, the rehabilitation process, including sheltered employment and social rehabilitation, is supportive; for others, however, any attempt at rehabilitation or socialization may cause intolerable stress (Wing, 1977). Therefore, mental health professionals should avoid adopting the philosophy that all their patients must ultimately become self-reliant in competitive employment and independent living and significantly improve their ability to socialize. At the same time, staff should remember that some patients who appear to have no potential and seem to be making no progress can, after long periods, sometimes measured in years, blossom and accomplish more than could have been predicted.

Mental health professionals also need to reconcile themselves to the fact that many patients will "opt out" and flee from rehabilitation efforts (Lamb, 1971b). Perhaps it is patients' feelings of inadequacy and fear of failure; perhaps they realize they will never be able to measure up to staff's expectations. Perhaps they fear losing their Supplemental Security Income, which provides a great deal of their sense of personal security.

In my opinion, staff make a major mistake if they demand, as some programs do, that patients must choose between participating in all of the program or none of it. Even if patients refuse to participate in social and vocational rehabilitation, staff should still offer them whatever services they will accept, even if it is only medication and crisis intervention. Sometimes these services are all the patient can handle at the time. If staff leave the door open, patients may return to avail themselves of other services in the future. If mental health staff do nothing more than help patients stabilize in the community, they are still making an important contribution to their lives.

Staff should offer patients rehabilitation, make it attractive to them, and even urge them to participate if in fact they possess sufficient ego strength. But if they do not and become symptomatic or begin to run from the staff's efforts, staff should reduce the pressure on patients and learn how to let them decline such activities gracefully and without fear of censure.

Staff Motivation and Needs

Mental health staff need—at first as part of their training and subsequently while on the job—to become aware of their own motivations for working in the helping professions. They should explore questions like these: What needs of mine are being met? Am I trying to fulfill needs at work that could or should be met elsewhere in my life?

Not that our own needs should never be met from our work with patients. But to what degree? Such motivations are rarely absent and are not necessarily bad—providing we are aware of their existence, keep them in moderation, and do not let them adversely affect our work with patients. More specifically, staff need to ask themselves: To what extent do I get vicarious gratification from my patients' accomplishments or acting out? How much does my sense of being productive depend on my bringing about "significant" change in my patients? To what extent am I in this field to get help for myself and to resolve my own problems? How much do I need to have contact with verbal, attractive patients and to be admired and loved by them?

If staff can resolve such questions for themselves, they may alleviate the problem of trying consciously or unconsciously to have patients meet their needs. There is a danger for all mental health staff, whether professional or paraprofessional, that patients will come to play too large a role in validating the staff's own worth. Inappropriate staff needs can also be a factor in unrealistic expectations of long-term patients. Healthy striving on the part of staff for a sense of productivity should not be denigrated, but staff should be reminded that there is a delicate balance between meeting their own needs and those of their patients. Enlisting patients to participate in the process of meeting our own needs in a way destructive to them may be an occupational hazard and, on a deeper level, may relate to our motivations for "helping" others. In any case, the disciplined therapist needs to reappraise these issues periodically throughout his "helping" career. A clear awareness of one's own motivation and needs can be a crucial factor in preventing disillusionment or burnout when long-term patients fail to meet our needs.

Meeting Dependency Needs

Another cause of staff burnout is confusion about the extent to which nurturing patients and meeting their dependency needs is desirable and appropriate. While it is generally taught that "good" patients "work" in treatment, for a sizable proportion of long-term patients the primary role of mental health staff may be to provide not therapy but support. It is especially important to provide support in the form of sheltered housing, sheltered work, sheltered social situations, and sustaining interpersonal relationships. While independence is generally preferable to dependence in our society, staff must become comfortable in gratifying dependency needs and realize that everyone, not just long-term patients, needs some degree of support. This support can be given without undermining the patient's push toward whatever level of autonomy he is capable of.

Since the dependency relationship can become burdensome, limits must be set on gratification of dependency needs. Patients must know that, except at times of crisis, it is inappropriate to call staff at all hours of the day and night. If staff members work as a team in treating long-term patients, the dependency relationship can be dispersed among members of the team. Thus we can avoid a relationship that may become exhausting for the professional, as well as more than the patient can handle.

Aside from such considerations, however, staff should remain aware of the basic moral disapproval in our society of dependency, of a passive, inactive life-style, and of accepting public support instead of working (see Chapter Two). Though it is often covert, such disapproval pervades all strata of our society; the mentally ill do not seem to be exempt from this disapproval. Perhaps no other factor is so likely to lead to staff resentment, unrealistic expectations, and, ultimately, burnout.

A Final Word

The seeds of staff burnout are planted when mental health professionals who work with long-term patients do not recognize that such patients vary greatly in their potential for rehabilitation. This situation leads to unrealistic expectations and frustration for staff. The concept of normalization, if misapplied, can lead to the same result. Contributing to the frustration is administrative pressure on staff to produce the impossible. Staff must be able to make clear, open decisions about their willingness to work with long-term patients. Then they will not be so likely to become frustrated and burned out and either abandon their long-term patients or unwittingly drive them away.

Summary of Treatment Issues

This book has been concerned with long-term severely disabled patients in the community—patients who in times past would have lived out their lives in state hospitals. In that sense, exploring ways to make deinstitutionalization work is what this book is about. When these patients were institutionalized in their "asylums," there seemed little need to understand them other than to give them a diagnosis. Now there is every reason to have an in-depth understanding not only of the patients themselves but also their interactions with their fellow citizens. In the old state hospitals, care was routinized; efforts were directed almost solely toward adapting the patients to hospital life. Now that they are in the community, liberated from the institutions that formerly enveloped them, their treatment should be given the highest priority. We must then confront the questions of how to treat them effectively, how to meet their many needs, how to raise their level of functioning, and how to enhance the quality of their lives.

Some Common Themes

We have seen that there is often a tendency to underestimate the value and humanizing effect of ex-hospital patients simply having their liberty to the extent they can handle it and of having free movement in the community. The great majority of long-term patients in the community now have this liberty, although they may not use it as we would. Even if their activity does not extend beyond taking walks in the neighborhood and going to supermarkets and fast-food chains, it is liberty, nonetheless, and fully as precious as ours is to us.

Still there are many who advocate that we repeat the mistakes of the past and return most of these patients to the hospitals where they can supposedly get treatment, activities, and care. But we can make community settings as high quality and treatment-oriented as we wish, and with a full range of activities. It depends on both society's priorities, as reflected in the level of mental health funding, and our own priorities within the mental health system, which together determine how much money we are able and willing to spend and how much effort we are willing to invest. For just a fraction of what it would cost to keep a person in a state hospital at today's level of funding we could indeed have high-quality care in the community. Further, we must avoid easy "solutions" such as those described in Chapter Three. They cannot substitute for money and hard work in community settings.

A pattern of neglect of the long-term severely mentally ill has long characterized our society and the mental health professions. This neglect may be rooted in professionals' dissatisfaction with meeting chronic dependency needs, society's disapproval of dependency, a distaste for the lower social classes, and an inclination, like that in the larger society, to exclude the mentally ill and maintain social distance from them. On the other hand, we have seen throughout this book that despite their powerful dependency needs and limited tolerance for stress, when attention is finally turned to the chronically mentally disabled, neglect often gives way to unrealistic expectations of rehabilitation. The training of mental health workers must be redirected so that they come to terms with their feelings about dependency, learn to tolerate chronic dependency, allow themselves to feel comfortable with gratifying appropriate dependency needs, and learn how to set realistic goals.

It has been a major theme of this book that we need to recognize that the long-term severely disabled have varying potentials for functioning. What is often thought to be a relatively homogeneous group in fact ranges from those who have the potential to function adequately in the community to those who cannot manage more than a passive undemanding life in a protected setting. Unrealistic expectations of these patients and of ourselves will only lead to their and our frustration and failure and ultimately to mutual abandonment of the effort.

Living Arrangements

We have seen that the very survival of long-term patients, not to mention their rehabilitation, begins with an appropriately supportive and structured living arrangement; other treatment and rehabilitation are of little avail until patients feel secure and stabilized in their living arrangements. We have also seen that on closer scrutiny this population turns out to be quite heterogeneous. Thus a wide variety of living arrangements are needed—with different degrees of support and structure, different intensities of interpersonal interaction and nurturing, and different kinds of programming. But it cannot be emphasized enough that, in order to have the quantity and quality of living arrangements and treatment and rehabilitation services we need, greatly increased funding must be made available.

This book has emphasized bringing services to patients when they will not come to our clinics, our day treatment centers, our aftercare programs, and our vocational and social rehabilitation programs. In Chapter Four we saw that half the patients in a board-and-care home would literally not walk down the block to attend a high-quality social rehabilitation program. There is therapeutic value for patients when they venture forth to attend programs outside their living situations; but what if they are unwilling or emotionally unable to do so? It may well be that long-term patients who function well in community mental health centers and community rehabilitation programs are in the minority of the total population of long-term patients when we include those hidden away in board-and-care homes, living alone, or residing with their families.

Since a large proportion of the chronically mentally ill live in nonmedical community residential facilities run by administrators and staff not specifically trained in the management of psychiatric patients, mental health professionals need to go out to residential facilities to provide consultation. Consultants need to know about licensing regulations, zoning problems, tenuous neighborhood relationships, and all the details of the facilities' clinical, administrative, and housekeeping procedures. They need to understand the wide range of social and vocational potentials of long-term patients and learn that certain patients need highly structured programs and facilities. Consultants should understand that facility administrators feel they are looked down upon by mental health professionals; they should also be aware of the problems that can arise when they attempt to provide both consultation and direct service to the same facility.

Consultants to residential facilities need to explain how to determine admission criteria, how to establish patient government, how to deal with the schizophrenic's difficulty in tolerating intimacy. They need to convey to staff the importance of setting limits, the rudiments of crisis management, methods of dealing with the problem of alcohol and drugs, and techniques for recognizing and managing antisocial personality disorders.

Another theme of this book has been the need to effectively serve that small proportion of the chronic population who require a high degree of structure and control. As Bachrach (1980a) states, the "least restrictive" environment is not necessarily the most therapeutic. Such persons lack the impulse control to manage their lives well enough to meet the demands of community living, even in a protected setting such as a board-and-care home. These patients who need structure are not unlike those found in the residual group of patients left behind in state hospitals after deinstitutionalization. They are characterized by some or all of the following traits: assaultive behavior; severe, overt, major psychopathology; reluctance to take psychotropic medications; inability to adjust to open settings; problems with drugs and alcohol in addition to mental illness; and self-destructive behavior.

An alternative to the state hospital has been described—the locked skilled-nursing facility with special programs for the mentally ill. Such a facility, when run properly, can offer all the advantages of a small, high-quality private hospital, but at less than half the per diem cost of the state hospital. These facilities give patients in need of structure a chance at treatment and rehabilitation in a setting in the patient's home community. The intensive program that schedules most of the patient's day is another key element in providing structure. Its relatively small size (hopefully less than one hundred beds) and high staff/patient ratio mean that every staff member can get to know every patient and thus create an individualized treatment milieu.

Focusing on the Underserved

Young chronic patients are faced with the same concerns and life-cycle stresses as others in their age group. They strive for independence, satisfying relationships, a sense of identity, and a realistic vocational choice. Lacking the ability to withstand stress and intimacy, they struggle and often repeatedly fail. The result is anxiety, depression, psychotic episodes, and hospitalization; gradually many begin to give up the struggle. Such concerns may become intensified during the reassessment of life that takes place at about age thirty. Denial of illness, the rebelliousness of youth, and issues of control and violence compound the problems. Since the advent of deinstitutionalization, patients can no longer take asylum from stresses in a lifetime of hospitalization. Many patients drift from city to city or from one living situation to another. Nevertheless there are ways of approaching these problems: working with young patients while they may still be motivated to make changes, helping them develop appropriate rationalizations, and supporting realistic goals. Further, in many instances we need to be patient. If we have an opportunity to see patients over long periods of time, we often find that we must wait for years, through repeated crises and many attempts, before we finally succeed in involving the patient with us.

We need to know who our friends are. Families of the mentally ill have begun to organize and have proven themselves determined, persistent, and effective advocates for services for the chronically and severely mentally ill. We should join with them in these efforts. At the same time, we should remember that at least half the long-term, severely disabled patients live with their families. By helping these families with our understanding, our attention and concern, and our advice, we can not only ease their burdens but also enlist them in common cause with us in the treatment and rehabilitation of their relatives—if we adopt an approach that is both sensitive to their needs and practical. As a beginning we should give practical, realistic advice on how to deal with the illness and offer empathy and support rather than placing blame. It has been a theme of this book that forming a partnership with families can be as important as anything we do in our efforts to better the lives of the long-term mentally ill in the community.

Has there been criminalization of the mentally ill? This complex question was examined in Chapter Nine. There is evidence suggesting a diversion of mental patients into the criminal justice system. Moreover, studies in recent years have shown that the arrest rates for ex-hospital patients are higher than those for the general population; there is some evidence the increased arrest rate is related to mental status. Moreover, those who would have been hospitalized before deinstitutionalization are now in the community and hence more subject to arrest. This is illustrated by a not uncommon occurrence. A paranoid schizophrenic feels that a perfect stranger is about to harm him; without provocation he assaults the stranger and is arrested. Had he been confined for life in a hospital there would have been no opportunity for this to happen.

Clearly the system of voluntary mental health outpatient treatment is inadequate for this population who are extremely resistant to it. If they do agree to accept treatment, they tend not to keep their appointments, not to take their medications, and to be least welcome at outpatient facilities. These patients cry out for control and structure, and we have a choice. We can allow them to lead chaotic lives in the community, characterized by frequent hospitalization, arrest, and intense anxiety, depression, and deprivation. Or when needed we can provide structure in the form of involuntary treatment, both inpatient and in the community, utilizing such mechanisms as conservatorship.

Individualizing Treatment

No theme of this book has been more important than the need to treat each patient as an individual with a unique personality and a unique set of problems. In the old state hospitals we did not; in the community we can see the same tendencies emerging—as, for instance, in impersonal case management systems and in group aftercare programs where the patient's uniqueness is lost. I have stressed the importance of both an individualized approach and also individual contact with patients, psychotherapy if you will, but therapy specifically designed to meet the needs of the long-term patient. These patients usually see themselves as helpless and incompetent (they sometimes delude themselves with a veneer of grandiosity). We need to give them a sense of mastery—the feeling that they can cope with their internal drives, their symptoms, and the demands of their environment. We need to be *active* in our interactions with these patients, to set limits and to give advice, and to help them put together the components of a community support system. We need to help them see that their psychotic symptoms are their way of reacting to stress, not simply mysterious, terrifying, all-powerful forces beyond their control; there are specific measures they can take to alleviate the situation, such as calling their therapist, trying to understand the precipitating stress, and increasing their medication. Therapy should be directed to strengthening ego controls; rationalization and guilt reduction should also be utilized when appropriate. The very real problems of the life cycle and existential concerns are often central factors in our work with long-term patients. That the mental health worker with the primary responsibility for individual patients needs a considerable amount of training goes without saying.

Other Treatment Issues

Although Supplemental Security Income (SSI) gives the psychiatrically disabled a dependable source of income and helps make it possible for them to live in the community, the secondary gain inherent in SSI may interfere with our efforts at social and vocational rehabilitation. For patients amenable to rehabilitation, adequate and appropriate rehabilitation services should be made available, not simply income maintenance. But we should be extremely careful to see that patients who cannot withstand the stress of such activities do not feel pressured to participate in them. Mental health professionals also have an important role to play in actively assisting that large proportion of the long-term mentally ill who require SSI to gain initial approval and then retain their eligibility.

A short-term, goal-oriented, day treatment center can provide a true alternative to acute hospitalization for long-term patients. But in order to accomplish this, the day treatment center needs to have clearly defined, time-limited goals and an orientation to the psycho-dynamics of the here and now. It needs to offer a comprehensive program including individual and group psychotherapy and meaningful activities. Adequate dosages of psychoactive medications need to be prescribed. Finally, involvement with the family is crucial, as are clearly defined staff roles and a close working relationship with an inpatient service.

The day treatment center also can serve as the hub of a network of services for long-term patients. The staff, by helping long-term patients through their time of greatest need—acute crisis—can use the relationship and trust thus developed to involve them in a community network of continuing rehabilitation and support after discharge from the day treatment center. Long-term patients need the sense of security that comes from knowing there is a support system in the community with a full range of services that can help sustain them in what often seems to be a frightening world full of overwhelming demands.

While we have seen throughout this book that the goal of "normalizing" the patient's living situation, social milieu, and work situation can often be unrealistic, we should pursue it when it is feasible. Social rehabilitation is a case in point. In the social rehabilitation process, as distinguished from other aspects of treatment and rehabilitation, mental health professionals can best serve as consultants; I believe that teachers, volunteers, recreation department personnel, librarians, and college students can do just as well and often better. Moreover, long-term patients need maximum contact with regular members of the community. This lessens their feelings they can associate only with other patients and mental health professionals and paraprofessionals specifically trained and paid to take care of them—as was the case in the hospital.

Staff burnout is not limited to mental health professionals who work with long-term patients, of course. But burnout is especially likely to occur when these workers do not recognize that their patients vary greatly in their potential for rehabilitation. This situation leads to unrealistic expectations, especially of patients whose potential is not high, and to frustration for staff. The concept of normalization, if misapplied, can lead to the same result. Contributing to the frustration is administrative pressure on staff to produce impossible results. Staff's ambivalence about gratifying their patients' dependency needs and uncertainty about their own needs and motivations can also lead to burnout.

Finally, I want to emphasize that working with long-term patients can be enjoyable and extremely gratifying. First, however, we must abandon our unrealistic expectations and redefine our notions of what constitutes progress with these patients. Sometimes it is returning them to the mainstream of life; sometimes it is raising their level of functioning just a little so they can work in a sheltered workshop. But oftentimes progress will have to be seen as simply helping a patient to lead a more satisfying and less oppressive life. If we can accept these patients as they are, we will indeed find that our relationships over the years with both them and their families become gratifying for us as well as therapeutic for them.

❧ References ❧

Abramson, M. F. "The Criminalization of Mentally Disordered Behavior." *Hospital and Community Psychiatry*, 1972, *23* (4), 101–105.

Alexander, F., French, T. M., Bacon, C. L., and others. *Psychoanalytic Therapy*. New York: Ronald Press, 1946.

Allen, P. "Care and Treatment of the Chronically Mentally Disabled in Residential Care Facilities." Article distributed at the quarterly meeting of the California Citizens Advisory Council, San Diego, October 1974.

Allen, P. "Clifford Beers: Toward a Realistic Sense of Hope." Address to the annual meeting of the California Association of Mental Health, Anaheim, 19 September 1975.

Allen, P. "A Bill of Rights for Citizens Using Outpatient Mental Health Services." In H. R. Lamb and Associates, *Community Survival for Long-Term Patients*. San Francisco: Jossey-Bass, 1976.

Althoff, J. G. "Time Limits in and Leave from a Day Treatment Program." *Hospital and Community Psychiatry*, 1980, *31* (12), 841–844.

Anderson, C. M., Hogarty, G., and Reiss, D. J. "The Psychoeducational Family Treatment of Schizophrenia." In M. J. Goldstein (Ed.), *New Directions for Mental Health Services: New Developments in Interventions with Families of Schizophrenics*, no. 12. San Francisco: Jossey-Bass, 1981.

Anderson, J. R. "Social Security and SSI Benefits for the Mentally Disabled." *Hospital and Community Psychiatry*, 1982, *33* (4), 295–298.

Andolfi, M. *Family Therapy: An Interactional Approach.* New York: Plenum, 1979.

Anthony, W. A. "Efficacy of Psychiatric Rehabilitation." *Psychological Bulletin,* 1972, *78,* 447-456.

Anthony, W. A., Cohen, M. R., and Vitalo, R. "The Measurement of Rehabilitation Outcome." *Schizophrenia Bulletin,* 1978, *4* (3), 365-383.

Appleton, W. S. "Mistreatment of Patients' Families by Psychiatrists." *American Journal of Psychiatry,* 1974, *131* (6), 655-657.

Appleton, W. S. "Fourth Psychoactive Drug Usage Guide." *Journal of Clinical Psychiatry,* 1982, *43* (1), 12-27.

Arieti, S. *Interpretation of Schizophrenia.* New York: Basic Books, 1974.

Arieti, S. "Psychiatric Controversy: Man's Ethical Dimension." *American Journal of Psychiatry,* 1975, *132* (1), 39-42.

Arnhoff, F. N. "Social Consequences of Policy Toward Mental Illness." *Science,* 1975, *27* (6), 1277-1281.

Arthur Bolton Associates. "A Study of the Need for and Availability of Mental Health Services for Mentally Disordered Jail Inmates and Juveniles in Detention Facilities." Report to the California State Legislature, Sacramento, October 1976. (Mimeograph.)

Bachrach, L. L. *Deinstitutionalization: An Analytical Review and Sociological Perspective.* Rockville, Md.: National Institute of Mental Health, 1976.

Bachrach, L. L. "A Conceptual Approach to Deinstitutionalization." *Hospital and Community Psychiatry,* 1978, *29* (9), 573-578.

Bachrach, L. L. "Planning Mental Health Services for Chronic Patients." *Hospital and Community Psychiatry,* 1979, *30* (6), 387-392.

Bachrach, L. L. "Is the Least Restrictive Environment Always the Best? Sociological and Semantic Implications." *Hospital and Community Psychiatry,* 1980a, *31* (2), 97-103.

Bachrach, L. L. "Overview: Model Programs for Chronic Mental Patients." *American Journal of Psychiatry,* 1980b, *137* (9), 1023-1031.

Bachrach, L. L. "Continuity of Care for Chronic Mental Patients: A Conceptual Analysis." *American Journal of Psychiatry,* 1981a, *138* (11), 1449-1456.

Bachrach, L. L. "A Conceptual Approach to Deinstitutionalization of the Mentally Retarded: A Perspective from the Experience of the Mentally Ill." In R. H. Bruininks, B. Best-Sigford, and K. C. Lakin (Eds.), *Deinstitutionalization and Community Adjustment of Developmentally Disabled Persons.* Minneapolis: University of Minnesota Press, 1981b.

Bachrach, L. L. "Young Adult Chronic Patients: An Analytical Review of the Literature." *Hospital and Community Psychiatry,* 1982, *33* (3), 189–197.

Baekeland, F., and Lundwall, L. "Dropping Out of Treatment: A Critical Review." *Psychological Bulletin,* 1975, *82,* 738–783.

Barter, J. T. "Successful Community Programming for the Chronic Mental Patient: Principles and Practices." In J. Talbott (Ed.), *The Chronic Mental Patient.* Washington, D.C.: American Psychiatric Association, 1978.

Bassuk, E. L., and Schoonover, S. C. "The Private General Hospital's Psychiatric Emergency Service in a Decade of Transition." *Hospital and Community Psychiatry,* 1981, *32* (3), 181–185.

Beard, J. H., Goertzel, V., and Pearce, A. J. "The Effectiveness of Activity Group Therapy with Chronically Regressed Adult Schizophrenics." *International Journal of Group Psychotherapy,* 1958, *8,* 123–136.

Beigel, A., and Feder, S. L. "Patterns of Utilization in Partial Hospitalization." *American Journal of Psychiatry,* 1970, *126* (3), 1267–1274.

Bennett, D. "Community Psychiatry." *British Journal of Psychiatry,* 1978, *132,* 209–220.

Bentz, W. K., Edgerton, J. W., and Kherlopian, M. "Perceptions of Mental Illness Among People in a Rural Area." *Mental Hygiene,* 1969, *53,* 459–465.

Berkowitz, R., and others. "Lowering Expressed Emotion in Relatives of Schizophrenics." In M. J. Goldstein (Ed.), *New Directions for Mental Health Services: New Developments in Interventions with Families of Schizophrenics,* no. 12. San Francisco: Jossey-Bass, 1981.

Bonovitz, J. C., and Bonovitz, J. S. "Diversion of the Mentally Ill into the Criminal Justice System: The Police Intervention Perspective." *American Journal of Psychiatry,* 1981, *138* (7), 973–976.

Borus, J. F. "Deinstitutionalization of the Chronically Mentally Ill." *New England Journal of Medicine,* 1981, *305* (6), 339–342.

Brill, H., and Patton, R. E. "Analysis of 1955–1956 Population Fall in New York State Mental Hospitals in the First Year of Large-Scale Use of Tranquilizing Drugs." *American Journal of Psychiatry,* 1957, *114,* 509–514.

Brooks, A.D. *Law, Psychiatry, and the Mental Health System.* Boston: Little, Brown, 1974.

Brooks, A. D. "The Impact of Law on Psychiatric Hospitalization: Onslaught or Imperative Reform?" In S. L. Halleck (Ed.), *New Directions for Mental Health Services: Coping with the Legal Onslaught,* no. 4. San Francisco: Jossey-Bass, 1979.

Brown, G. W., Birley, J.L.T., and Wing, J. K. "Influence of Family Life on the Course of Schizophrenic Disorders: A Replication." *British Journal of Psychiatry,* 1972, *121,* 241–258.

Brown, G. W., Bone, M., Dalison, B., and Wing, J. K. *Schizophrenia and Social Care.* London: Oxford University Press, 1966.

Budson, R. D. *The Psychiatric Halfway House: A Handbook of Theory and Practice.* Pittsburgh: University of Pittsburgh Press, 1978.

Caplan, G. *The Theory and Practice of Mental Health Consultation.* New York: Basic Books, 1970.

Carlson, D. A., and others. "Problems in Treating the Lower-Class Psychotic." *Archives of General Psychiatry,* 1965, *13* (3), 269–274.

Carmichael, D. M. "Day Hospital Program with Emphasis on Translatable Skills." In R. L. Epps and L. D. Hanes (Eds.), *Day Care of Psychiatric Patients.* Springfield, Ill.: Thomas, 1964.

Chamberlin, J. *On Our Own: Patient-Controlled Alternatives to the Mental Health System.* New York: Hawthorn Books, 1978.

Cherniss, C. *Staff Burnout.* Beverly Hills: Sage, 1980.

Creer, C., and Wing, J. K. *Schizophrenia at Home.* London: National Schizophrenia Fellowship, 1974.

Crocetti, G., Spiro, H. R., and Siassi, I. "Are the Ranks Closed? Attitudinal Social Distance and Mental Illness." *American Journal of Psychiatry,* 1971, *127,* 1121–1127.

Cross, K. W., Hassall, C., and Gath, D. "Psychiatric Day Care: The New Chronic Population?" *British Journal of Preventive and Social Medicine,* 1972, *26,* 199–204.

Cumming, E., and Cumming, J. *Closed Ranks: An Experiment in Mental Health Education.* Cambridge, Mass.: Harvard University Press, 1957.

Cutler, D. L., and Beigel, A. "A Church-Based Program of Community Activities for Chronic Patients." *Hospital and Community Psychiatry,* 1978, *29* (8), 497–501.

Cuvelier, F. "Patterns of Interaction Between Mental Patient and Caretaker." Paper presented at International Symposium on Foster Family Care, Geel, Belgium, 16 May 1975.

D'Arcy, C., and Brockman, J. "Changing Public Recognition of Psychiatric Symptoms? Blackfoot Revisited." *Journal of Health and Social Behavior,* 1976, *17,* 302–310.

Davis, J. M. "Overview: Maintenance Therapy in Psychiatry: I. Schizophrenia." *American Journal of Psychiatry,* 1975, *132* (12), 1237–1245.

Davis, L. A., and Peterson, C. L. "Training for and Consultation to Community Care Facilities." *Creedmoor Journal of Urban Psychiatry,* in press.

De Lott, F. "Societal Income Versus Willingness to Succeed." Paper presented at the National Conference of the International Association of Psycho-Social Rehabilitation Services, Chicago, 14–17 October 1976.

Department of Health and Human Services Steering Committee on the Chronically Mentally Ill. "Toward a National Plan for the Chronically Mentally Ill: Report to the Secretary, December 1980." DHHS publication (ADM) 81-1077. Rockville, Md.: Department of Health and Human Services, 1981.

Detre, T. P., and Jarecki, H. G. *Modern Psychiatric Treatment.* Philadelphia: Lippincott, 1971.

Deutsch, A. *The Shame of the States.* New York: Harcourt Brace Jovanovich, 1948.

Dincin, J. "Psychiatric Rehabilitation." *Schizophrenia,* 1975, *13,* 131–147.

Doll, W. "Family Coping with the Mentally Ill: An Unanticipated Problem of Deinstitutionalization." *Hospital and Community Psychiatry,* 1976, *27* (3), 183–185.

Dorwart, R. A. "Deinstitutionalization: Who Is Left Behind?" *Hospital and Community Psychiatry,* 1980, *31* (5), 336–338.

Eisdorfer, C., and Batton, L. "The Mental Health Consultant as Seen by His Consultees." *Community Mental Health Journal*, 1972, *8* (3), 171–177.

Emener, W. G., Jr. "Professional Burnout: Rehabilitation's Hidden Handicap." *Journal of Rehabilitation*, 1979, *45* (1), 55–58.

Erickson, R. C., and Backus, F. I. "Symptom Severity and Day Hospital Admission." *Hospital and Community Psychiatry*, 1973, *24* (2), 102–104.

Estroff, S. E. *Making It Crazy: An Ethnography of Psychiatric Clients in an American Community*. Berkeley: University of California Press, 1981.

Fairweather, G. W. (Ed.). *Social Psychology in Treating Mental Illness*. New York: Wiley, 1964.

Fairweather, G. W. "The Fairweather Lodge: A Twenty-Five Year Retrospective." In G. W. Fairweather (Ed.), *New Directions for Mental Health Services: The Fairweather Lodge: A Twenty-Five Year Retrospective*, no. 7. San Francisco: Jossey-Bass, 1980.

Fairweather, G. W., Sanders, D. H., Maynard, H., and Cressler, D. L. *Community Life for the Mentally Ill: An Alternative to Institutional Care*. Chicago: Aldine, 1969.

Falloon, I.R.H., and others. "Family Management Training in the Community Care of Schizophrenia." In M. J. Goldstein (Ed.), *New Directions for Mental Health Services: New Developments In Interventions with Families of Schizophrenics*, no. 12. San Francisco: Jossey-Bass, 1981.

Fenichel, O. *The Psychoanalytic Theory of Neurosis*. London: Routledge & Kegan Paul, 1946.

Fox, R. P. "Therapeutic Environments." *Archives of General Psychiatry*, 1973a, *29* (2), 514–517.

Fox, R. P. "Using Inpatient Staff for Aftercare of Severely Disturbed Chronic Patients." *Hospital and Community Psychiatry*, 1973b, *24* (7), 482–484.

General Accounting Office. *Returning the Mentally Disabled to the Community: Government Needs to Do More*. Washington, D.C.: General Accounting Office, 1978.

Glasscote, R. M., Cumming, E., Rutman, I., Sussex, J. N., and Glassman, S. M. *Rehabilitating the Mentally Ill in the Community*. Washington, D.C.: Joint Information Service of American

Psychiatric Association and National Association for Mental Health, 1971.

Goldman, H. H., Gattozzi, A. A., and Taube, C. A. "Defining and Counting the Chronically Mentally Ill." *Hospital and Community Psychiatry*, 1981, *32* (1), 21-27.

Goldstein, M. J., and Kopeikin, H. S. "Short- and Long-Term Effects of Combining Drug and Family Therapy." In M. J. Goldstein (Ed.) *New Directions for Mental Health Services: New Developments in Interventions with Families of Schizophrenics*, no. 12. San Francisco: Jossey-Bass, 1981.

Gootnick, I. "The Psychiatric Day Center in the Treatment of the Chronic Schizophrenic." *American Journal of Psychiatry*, 1971, *128* (4), 485-488.

Greenblatt, M. "The Third Revolution Defined: It Is Sociopolitical." *Psychiatric Annals*, 1977, 7, 506-509.

Grunberg, F., Klinger, B. I., and Grument, B. R. "Homicide and the Deinstitutionalization of the Mentally Ill." *American Journal of Psychiatry*, 1977, *134* (6), 685-687.

Gunderson, J. G. "Controversies About the Psychotherapy of Schizophrenia." *American Journal of Psychiatry*, 1973, *130* (6), 677-681.

Gunderson, J. G. "Patient-Therapist Matching: A Research Evaluation." *American Journal of Psychiatry*, 1978, *135* (10), 1193-1197.

Halpern, J., Binner, P. R., Mohr, C. B., and others. *The Illusion of Deinstitutionalization*. Denver: Denver Research Institute, 1978.

Herz, M. I., and others. "Day Versus Inpatient Hospitalization: A Controlled Study." *American Journal of Psychiatry*, 1971, *127* (4), 1371-1381.

Hogarty, G. E. "The Plight of Schizophrenics in Modern Treatment Programs." *Hospital and Community Psychiatry*, 1971, *22* (7), 197-203.

Hogarty, G. E., and Ulrich, R. F. "Temporal Effects of Drug and Placebo in Delaying Relapse in Schizophrenic Outpatients." *Archives of General Psychiatry*, 1977, *34* (3), 297-301.

Hogarty, G. E., and others. "Who Goes There?—A Critical Evaluation of Admissions to a Psychiatric Day Hospital." *American Journal of Psychiatry*, 1968, *124* (1), 934-944.

Hollingshead, A. B., and Redlich, F. C. *Social Class and Mental Illness: A Community Study.* New York: Wiley, 1958.

James, J. F., and others. "Psychiatric Morbidity in Prisons." *Hospital and Community Psychiatry,* 1980, *31* (10), 674–677.

Jarvis, P. E., and Nelson, S. E. "Familiarization: A Vital Step in Mental Health Consultation." *Community Mental Health Journal,* 1967, *3* (4), 343–348.

Johnstone, E. C., and others. "Institutionalization and the Defects of Schizophrenia." *British Journal of Psychiatry,* 1981, *139,* 195–203.

Joint Commission on Mental Illness and Health. *Action for Mental Health: Final Report of the Commission.* New York: Basic Books, 1961.

Kahn, R. "Job Burnout (Prevention and Remedies)." *Public Welfare,* Spring 1978, pp. 61–63.

Kanter, J. "Coping Strategies for Relatives of the Mentally Ill." Paper presented at Threshold, Kensington, Maryland, 10 November 1980.

Kirk, S. A., and Therrien, M. E. "Community Mental Health Myths and the Fate of Former Hospitalized Patients." *Psychiatry,* 1975, *38* (3), 209–217.

Krawiecka, M., Goldberg, D., and Vaughan, M. "A Standardized Psychiatric Assessment Scale for Rating Chronic Psychotic Patients." *Acta Psychiatrica Scandinavica,* 1977, *55,* 299–308.

Kris, E. B. "The Role of Drugs in After-Care, Home-Care, and Maintenance." In C. Shagass (Ed.), *Modern Problems of Pharmacopsychiatry: The Role of Drugs in Community Psychiatry.* Vol. 6. Basel: Karger, 1971.

La Commare, P. L. "The Day Treatment Center: A Community Alternative to State Hospitalization." *Psychiatric Annals,* 1975, *5,* 178–183.

Lamb, H. R. "Chronic Psychiatric Patients in the Day Hospital." *Archives of General Psychiatry,* 1967a, *17* (11), 615–621.

Lamb, H. R. "Coordination: The Key to Rehabilitation." *Hospital and Community Psychiatry,* 1971a, *22* (2), 46–47.

Lamb, H. R. "Essential Concepts." In H. R. Lamb and Associates, *Rehabilitation in Community Mental Health.* San Francisco: Jossey-Bass, 1971b.

Lamb, H. R. "Treating Long-Term Schizophrenic Patients in the Community." In L. Bellak and H. H. Barten (Eds.), *Progress in Community Mental Health.* Vol. 3. New York: Brunner/Mazel, 1975.

Lamb, H. R. "Guiding Principles for Community Survival." In H. R. Lamb and Associates, *Community Survival for Long-Term Patients.* San Francisco: Jossey-Bass, 1976.

Lamb, H. R. "The State Hospital: Facility of Last Resort." *American Journal of Psychiatry,* 1977, *134* (10), 1151-1152.

Lamb, H. R. "Roots of Neglect of the Long-Term Mentally Ill." *Psychiatry,* 1979a, *41* (3), 201-207.

Lamb, H. R. "The New Asylums in the Community." *Archives of General Psychiatry,* 1979b, *36* (2), 129-134.

Lamb, H. R. "Staff Burnout in Work with Long-Term Patients." *Hospital and Community Psychiatry,* 1979c, *30* (6), 396-398.

Lamb, H. R. "Board-and-Care Home Wanderers." *Archives of General Psychiatry,* 1980a, *37* (2), 135-137.

Lamb, H. R. "Structure: The Neglected Ingredient of Community Treatment." *Archives of General Psychiatry,* 1980b, *37* (11), 1224-1228.

Lamb, H. R. "Securing Patients' Rights—Responsibly." *Hospital and Community Psychiatry,* 1981, *32* (6), 393-397.

Lamb, H. R., and Associates. *Rehabilitation in Community Mental Health.* San Francisco: Jossey-Bass, 1971.

Lamb, H. R., and Associates. *Community Survival for Long-Term Patients.* San Francisco: Jossey-Bass, 1976.

Lamb, H. R., and Edelson, M. B. "The Carrot and the Stick: Inducing Local Programs to Serve Long-Term Patients." *Community Mental Health Journal, 1976, 12* (2), 137-144.

Lamb, H. R., and Goertzel, V. "Discharged Mental Patients—Are They Really in the Community?" *Archives of General Psychiatry,* 1971, *24* (1), 29-34.

Lamb, H. R., and Goertzel, V. "The Demise of the State Hospital— A Premature Obituary?" *Archives of General Psychiatry,* 1972a, *26* (6), 489-495.

Lamb, H. R., and Goertzel, V. "High Expectations of Long-Term Ex-State Hospital Patients." *American Journal of Psychiatry,* 1972b, *129,* 471-475.

Lamb, H. R., and Goertzel, V. "The Long-Term Patient in the Era of Community Treatment." *Archives of General Psychiatry*, 1977, *34* (6), 679–682.

Lamb, H. R., and Odenheimer, J. "The Day Hospital." In H. R. Lamb, D. Heath, and J. J. Downing (Eds.), *Handbook of Community Mental Health Practice: The San Mateo Experience*. San Francisco: Jossey-Bass, 1969.

Lamb, H. R., and Oliphant, E. "Parents of Schizophrenics: Advocates for the Mentally Ill." In L. I. Stein (Ed.), *New Directions for Mental Health Services: Community Support Systems for the Long-Term Patient*, no. 2. San Francisco: Jossey-Bass, 1979.

Lamb, H. R., Sorkin, A. P., and Zusman, J. "Legislating Social Control of the Mentally Ill in California." *American Journal of Psychiatry*, 1981, *138* (3), 334–339.

Lamb, H. R., and Zusman, J. "A New Look at Primary Prevention." *Hospital and Community Psychiatry*, 1981, *32* (12), 843–848.

Lemkau, P. V., and Crocetti, G. M. "An Urban Population's Opinion and Knowledge About Mental Illness." *American Journal of Psychiatry*, 1962, *118* (8), 692–700.

Lidz, T. *The Person: His Develoment Throughout the Life Cycle.* New York: Basic Books, 1968.

Liebman, L. "The Definition of Disability in Social Security and Supplemental Security Income: Drawing the Bounds of Social Welfare Estates." *Harvard Law Review*, 1976, *89*, 833–867.

Linn, M. W. "Can Foster Care Survive?" In R. D. Budson (Ed.), *New Directions for Mental Health Services: Issues in Community Residential Care*, no. 11. San Francisco: Jossey-Bass, 1981.

Linn, M. W., Klett, C. J., and Caffey, E. M., Jr. "Foster Home Characteristics and Psychiatric Patient Outcome." *Archives of General Psychiatry*, 1980, *37* (2), 129–132.

Linn, M. W., and others. "Day Treatment and Psychotropic Drugs in the Aftercare of Schizophrenic Patients." *Archives of General Psychiatry*, 1979, *36* (9), 1055–1066.

Lourie, N. V. "The Many Faces of Advocacy." In I. N. Berlin (Ed.), *Advocacy for Child Mental Health*. New York: Brunner/Mazel, 1975.

Ludwig, A. M. *Treating the Treatment Failures*. New York: Grune & Stratton, 1971.

Mackota, C. "Using Work Therapeutically." In H. R. Lamb and Associates, *Community Survival for Long-Term Patients.* San Francisco: Jossey-Bass, 1976.

Marmor, J. "The Crisis of Middle Age." *Psychiatry Digest,* 1968, *29,* 17-21.

May, P.R.A. "Modifying Health-Care Services for Schizophrenic Patients." *Hospital and Community Psychiatry,* 1969, *20,* 363-368.

Mechanic, D. "Alternatives to Mental Hospital Treatment: A Sociological Perspective." In L. I. Stein and M. A. Test (Eds.), *Alternatives to Mental Hospital Treatment.* New York: Plenum, 1978.

Melvile, C., Kibler, J., and Haddle, H. *The Balanced Service System.* Atlanta: Georgia Mental Health Institute, 1977.

Mendel, W. M. *Supportive Care.* Los Angeles: Mara Books, 1975.

Mendel, W. M. "Staff Burn-Out: Diagnosis, Treatment, and Prevention." In L. I. Stein (Ed.), *New Directions for Mental Health Services: Community Support Systems for the Long-Term Patient,* no. 2. San Francisco: Jossey-Bass, 1979.

Messier, M., and others. "A Follow-Up Study of Intensively Treated Chronic Schizophrenic Patients." *American Journal of Psychiatry,* 1969, *125* (2), 1123-1127.

Meyer, J. K. "Attitudes Toward Mental Illness in a Maryland Community." *Public Health Report,* 1964, *79,* 769-772.

Moise, L. E. "Will the Real Advocate for the Retarded Please Stand Up?" *Child Welfare,* 1975, *54,* 27-33.

Murphy, H.B.M., Engelsmann, F., and Tcheng-Laroche, F. "The Influence of Foster-Home Care of Psychiatric Patients." *Archives of General Psychiatry,* 1976, *33,* 179-183.

Myers, J. K., and Bean, L. L. *A Decade Later: A Follow-Up of Social Class and Mental Illness.* New York: Wiley, 1968.

Neffinger, G. G. "The Evolution of an Acute Day Treatment Program." *Hospital and Community Psychiatry,* 1980, *31* (12), 826-828.

Ognyanov, V., and Cowen, L. "A Day Hospital Program for Patients in Crisis." *Hospital and Community Psychiatry,* 1974, *25* (4), 209-210.

Parsons, T. *The Social System.* New York: Free Press, 1951.

Paul, G. L. "The Implementation of Effective Treatment Programs for Chronic Mental Patients: Obstacles and Recommendations."

In J. A. Talbott (Ed.), *The Chronic Mental Patient*. Washington, D.C.: American Psychiatric Association, 1978.

Paul, G. L., and Lentz, R. J. *Psychosocial Treatment of Chronic Mental Patients: Milieu Versus Social Learning Programs*. Cambridge, Mass.: Harvard University Press, 1977.

Pepper, B., Kirshner, M. C., and Ryglewicz, H. "The Young Adult Chronic Patient: Overview of a Population." *Hospital and Community Psychiatry*, 1981, *32* (7), 463–469.

Pepper, B., and Ryglewicz, H. (Eds.). *New Directions for Mental Health Services: The Young Adult Chronic Patient*, no. 14. San Francisco: Jossey-Bass, 1982.

Peterson, C. L. "Consultation with Community Care Facilities." *Social Work in Health Care*, 1976, *2*, 181–191.

Peterson, C. L. "Consultation to Residential Facilities." In A. S. Rogawski (Ed.), *New Directions for Mental Health Services: Mental Health Consultation in Community Settings*, no. 3. San Francisco: Jossey-Bass, 1979.

Phillips, D. L. "Public Identification and Acceptance of the Mentally Ill." *American Journal of Public Health*, 1966, *56*, 755–763.

Pines, A., and Maslach, C. "Characteristics of Staff Burnout in Mental Health Settings." *Hospital and Community Psychiatry*, 1978, *29* (4), 233–237.

Quen, J. M. "Asylum Psychiatry, Neurology, Social Work, and Mental Health: An Exploratory Study in Interprofessional History." *Journal of History of Behavioral Sciences*, 1977, *13*, 3–11.

Rabkin, J. "Public Attitudes Toward Mental Illness: A Review of the Literature." *Schizophrenia*, 1974, *10*, 9–33.

Rachlin, S., Pam, A., and Milton, J. "Civil Liberties versus Involuntary Hospitalization." *American Journal of Psychiatry*, 1975, *132* (2), 189–192.

Reich, R. "The Chronically Mentally Ill: Their Fate in New York City." *Bulletin of the New York State District Branch of the American Psychiatric Association*, 1972 (Nov.), p. 6.

Reich, R., and Siegel, L. "Psychiatry Under Siege: The Chronically Mentally Ill Shuffle to Oblivion." *Psychiatric Annals*, 1973, *3*, 35–55.

Reynolds, D. K., and Farberow, N. L. *Endangered Hope: Experiences in Psychiatric Aftercare Facilities*. Los Angeles: University of California Press, 1977.

Rock, R. S., Jacobson, M. A., and Janotaul, R. M. *Hospitalization and Discharge of the Mentally Ill.* Chicago: University of Chicago Press, 1968.

Roman, M., and Schmais, A. "Consumer Participation and Control: A Conceptual Overview." In L. Bellak and H. H. Barten (Eds.), *Progress in Community Mental Health.* New York: Grune & Stratton, 1972.

Roth, L. H. "Mental Health Commitment: The State of the Debate, 1980." *Hospital and Community Psychiatry,* 1980, *31* (6), 385–396.

Sadoff, R. L. "Criminal Behavior Masking Mental Illness." *Corrective Psychiatry and Journal of Social Therapy,* 1971, *17,* 41–47.

Scherl, D. J., and Macht, L. B. "Deinstitutionalization in the Absence of Consensus." *Hospital and Community Psychiatry,* 1979, *30* (9), 599–604.

Schiff, S. K. "Community Accountability and Mental Health Services." *Mental Hygiene,* 1970, *54,* 205–214.

Schwartz, S. R., and Goldfinger, S. M. "The New Chronic Patient: Clinical Characteristics of an Emerging Subgroup." *Hospital and Community Psychiatry,* 1981, *32* (7), 470–474.

Segal, S. P., and Aviram, U. *The Mentally Ill in Community-Based Sheltered Care.* New York: Wiley, 1978.

Serban, G., and Gidynski, C. B. "Differentiating Criteria for Acute–Chronic Distinction in Schizophrenia." *Archives of General Psychiatry,* 1975, *32* (6), 705–712.

Serban, G., and Woloshin, G. "Relationship Between Pre- and Post-Morbid Psychological Stress in Schizophrenics." *Psychological Reports,* 1974, *35,* 507–517.

Shadish, W. R., Jr., and Bootzin, R. R. "Nursing Homes and Chronic Mental Patients." *Schizophrenia Bulletin,* 1981, *7* (3), 488–498.

Shadoan, R. A. "Making Board and Care Homes Therapeutic." In H. R. Lamb and Associates, *Community Survival for Long-Term Patients.* San Francisco: Jossey-Bass, 1976.

Sheets, J. L., Prevost, J. A., and Reihman, J. "The Young Adult Chronic Patient: Three Hypothesized Subgroups." In B. Pepper and H. Ryglewicz (Eds.), *New Directions for Mental Health Services: The Young Adult Chronic Patient,* no. 14. San Francisco: Jossey-Bass, 1982.

Siassi, I., Spiro, H. R., and Crocetti, G. "The Social Acceptance of the Ex-Mental Hospital Patient." *Community Mental Health Journal*, 1973, *9*, 223–243.

Silverman, W. H., and Val, E. "The Day Hospital in the Context of a Community Mental Health Program." *Community Mental Health Journal*, 1975, *11* (1), 82–90.

Simon, W. B. "On Reluctance to Leave the Public Mental Hospital." *Psychiatry*, 1965, *28*, 145–156.

Solomon, E. B., and others. "Assessing the Community Care of Chronic Psychotic Patients." *Hospital and Community Psychiatry*, 1980, *31* (2), 113–116.

Sosowsky, L. "Crime and Violence Among Mental Patients Reconsidered in View of the New Legal Relationship Between the State and the Mentally Ill." *American Journal of Psychiatry*, 1978, *135* (1), 33–42.

Sosowsky, L. "Explaining the Increased Arrest Rate Among Mental Patients: A Cautionary Note." *American Journal of Psychiatry*, 1980, *137* (12), 1602–1605.

Spiegler, M., and Agigian, H. *Schools for Living*. New York: Brunner/Mazel, 1977.

Spivack, G., and others. "The Long-Term Patient in the Community: Life Style Patterns and Treatment Implications." *Hospital and Community Psychiatry*, 1982, *33* (4), 291–295.

Srole, L. "Geel, Belgium: The Natural Therapeutic Community." In G. Serbin and B. Astrachan (Eds.), *New Trends of Psychiatry in the Community*. Cambridge, Mass.: Ballinger, 1977.

Steadman, H. J., and Ribner, S. A. "Changing Perceptions of the Mental Health Needs of Inmates in Local Jails." *American Journal of Psychiatry*, 1980, *137* (9), 1115–1116.

Steadman, H. J., Vanderwyst, D., and Ribner, S. "Comparing Arrest Rates of Mental Patients and Criminal Offenders." *American Journal of Psychiatry*, 1978, *135* (10), 1218–1220.

Stein, L. I., Test, M. A., and Marx, A. J. "Alternative to the Hospital: A Controlled Study." *American Journal of Psychiatry*, 1975, *132* (5), 517–522.

Stern, R., and Minkoff, K. "Paradoxes in Programming for Chronic Patients in a Community Clinic." *Hospital and Community Psychiatry*, 1979, *30* (9), 613–617.

Stone, A. A. *Mental Health and Law: A System in Transition.* Rockville, Md.: National Institute of Mental Health, 1975.

Stone, A. A. "The Myth of Advocacy." *Hospital & Community Psychiatry,* 1979, *30* (12), 819–822.

Swank, G. E., and Winer, D. "Occurrence of Psychiatric Disorder in a County Jail Population." *American Journal of Psychiatry,* 1976, *133* (11), 1331–1336.

Talbott, J. A. (Ed.). *The Chronic Mental Patient: Problems, Solutions, and Recommendations for a Public Policy.* Washington, D.C.: American Psychiatric Association, 1978.

Talbott, J. A. "Deinstitutionalization: Avoiding the Disasters of the Past." *Hospital and Community Psychiatry,* 1979, *30* (9), 621–624.

Talbott, J. A. (Ed.). *The Chronic Mentally Ill: Treatment, Programs, Systems.* New York: Human Sciences Press, 1981.

Test, M. A. "Continuity of Care in Community Treatment." In L. I. Stein (Ed.), *New Directions for Mental Health Services: Community Support Systems for the Long-Term Patient,* no. 2. San Francisco: Jossey-Bass, 1979.

Test, M. A., and Stein, L. I. "Special Living Arrangements: A Model for Decision-Making." *Hospital and Community Psychiatry,* 1977, *28,* 608–610.

Test, M. A., and Stein, L. I. "Community Treatment of the Chronic Patient: Research Overview." *Schizophrenia Bulletin,* 1978, *4* (3), 350–364.

Thomas, S. "A Survey of the Relative Importance of Community Care Facility Characteristics to Different Consumer Groups." Paper presented at the meeting of the Midwestern Psychological Association, St. Louis, 1980.

Tringo, J. L. "The Hierarchy of Preference Toward Disability Groups." *Journal of Special Education,* 1970, *4,* 295–306.

Urmer, A. *A Study of California's New Mental Health Law.* Chatsworth, Calif.: ENKI Research Institute, 1971.

Van Putten, T., Crumpton, E., and Yale, C. "Drug Refusal in Schizophrenia and the Wish to Be Crazy." *Archives of General Psychiatry,* 1976, *33,* 1443–1446.

Vaughn, C. E., and Leff, J. P. "The Influence of Family and Social Factors on the Course of Psychiatric Illness: A Comparison of Schizophrenic and Depressed Neurotic Patients." *British Journal of Psychiatry,* 1976, *27* (8), 125–137.

Weinman, B., and Kleiner, R. J. "The Impact of Community Living and Community Member Intervention on the Adjustment of the Chronic Psychotic Patient." In L. I. Stein and M. A. Test (Eds.), *Alternatives to Mental Health Treatment.* New York: Plenum, 1978.

Whitehorn, J. C., and Betz, B. J. *Effective Psychotherapy with the Schizophrenic Patient.* New York: Aronson, 1975.

Whitmer, G. E. "From Hospitals to Jails: The Fate of California's Deinstitutionalized Mentally Ill." *American Journal of Orthopsychiatry,* 1980, *50,* 65–75.

Wing, J. K. "The Management of Schizophrenia in the Community." Paper presented at the annual meeting of the American College of Psychiatrists, Atlanta, February 1977.

Wing, J. K., and Brown, G. W. *Institutionalism and Schizophrenia.* New York: Cambridge University Press, 1970.

Wolfensberger, W. *Citizen Advocacy for the Handicapped, Impaired, and Disadvantaged: An Overview.* Washington, D.C.: U.S. Government Printing Office, 1972.

Wolkon, G. H. "Role Discontinuity and Resocialization of the Psychiatric Patient." *Social Science and Medicine,* 1970, *3,* 679–687.

Wolkon, G. H. "Changing Roles: Crises in the Continuum of Care in the Community." *Psychotherapy: Theory, Research and Practice,* 1974, *11* (4), 367–370.

Yalom, I. D. *Existential Psychotherapy.* New York: Basic Books, 1980.

Yin, R. K., and others. *Citizen Organizations: Increasing Client Control over Services.* Washington, D.C.: Rand Corporation, 1973.

Zitrin, A., Hardesty, A. S., and Burdock, E. T. "Crime and Violence Among Mental Patients." *American Journal of Psychiatry,* 1976, *133* (2), 142–149.

Zusman, J., and Lamb, H. R. "In Defense of Community Mental Health." *American Journal of Psychiatry,* 1977, *134,* 887–890.

❦ Index ❧